Miracles of Nature

By the same author

MARVELS OF NATURE

Miracles
of Nature

by

Per Hafslund

Evans Brothers Limited, London

Published by
Evans Brothers Limited
Montague House, Russell Square
London, W. C. 1

Set in 12 on 16 point Imprint and printed in Norway
by Dreyer Aksjeselskap, Stavanger, on art paper made by Saugbrugsforeningen, Halden.
All photographs by the author. Adaption and layout by Truls Hoff, Oslo.
7/5782

My Third Eye

'You are hopelessly in love with an inanimate object.' This remark, which I have never forgotten, was made many years ago by one of my best friends when I had declined an offer to go fishing with him, in order to concentrate on taking some photographs.

I wasn't at all insulted. I remember that remark, too, because my friend was right to some extent. I *was* quite captivated by my camera at the time. But I was happy with it – it was far from inanimate to me.

On the contrary it possessed magic powers. These powers attracted me at all times, to the despair of my family and friends.

Thinking back on it, I can see I was more completely captivated than I then realised. In my defense I might mention that I had just learned to use a camera with some proficiency. With my third eye, a magic eye, I was able to look into a new world which my studies so far had barely let me comprehend.

I became a photographer-zoologist. As such, one leads a strange double life, undulating helplessly between inspiration and exhaustion, vision and confusion, victory and defeat, while at the same time trying to attend to one's job and to appear outwardly normal. Zoologist and photographer become Siamese twins, as unfortunately one cannot rest while the other works. The fact that many animals make night-time their 'day', adds to the confusion.

The zoologist who is a photographer knows *where* the animals are, *when* they are there and *what* they are doing – or he can find this out. And his camera can often see things that he doesn't see, or perhaps doesn't know until the photographic film reveals it to him.

To explore animal life and lore through the eye of the camera, one should approach nature with the real eyes open and a humble mind. It is most important to listen and to learn to understand nature's own tune. The quiet naturalist with his simple camera may get more successful pictures than the well equipped, cocky optimist who believes in modern super-equipment alone.

Moderation is also important – but that is self-evident. Expense will limit the quantity for most enthusiasts – and the limitless number of possible subjects enforces restraint or specialisation.

Modern photographic techniques have given us incredible possibilities to learn more about life in its natural state. My advice to you who feel the yearning is to learn from those who know more – and to curb your ambition.

Even the simplest camera can take excellent pictures – and with complicated and expensive equipment it is possible to ruin the best subjects. Yet who can tell what the future may bring in this field? Let me just say that *today* no equipment is more important than the photographer himself – who sees with his third eye.

The Owls in the Avenue Trees

Late one night one of my students called to tell me that the police had been asked to destroy the owls that lived in the trees in the nearby avenue. A few days earlier a lady walking peacefully along the road had had her hat torn off her head, and shortly afterwards, a man got his head badly scratched. The newspapers had been full of stories about the vicious owls – for whom the bells now tolled.

The situation was indeed serious, as owls can be dangerous to humans. I have heard of a mother owl that flew straight into the face of a man and tore out an eye. But didn't the police know that there were owlets in the nest and that they couldn't look after themselves alone? And didn't the police know that in Norway the tawny owl is protected all the year round and must not be killed?

No, the police were unaware of the first fact and had overlooked the second. This put the matter in a different light, but what were they to do?

I suggested that, with two or three of my students, I should assume responsibility for the owl family. The law was more than satisfied with this, on the condition that the owls be removed within two days.

This was easier said than done. An agile youngster would have no difficulty getting up to the nest, fifteen to twenty feet above the ground, but how were we to get the adult owls to come with us?

We made one attempt after school the next day. One of the boys climbed the elm, but he was no more than six feet up when the mother owl lightly and soundlessly flew away. The boy was so surprised that he almost let go his grip on the branches. He thought that owls never fly in the daylight.

9

The tree-lined avenue at the end of February, the time when eggs are hatched. In Norway the winter can still be severe.

The boy resumed his climbing but I told him to come down again, as we couldn't very well take the nest away without at least one of the parents. By now he had reached the nest and couldn't resist the temptation to peer down into it: 'I can see three pairs of black eyes!'

'That's fine,' I answered. 'Now get down at once.'

We wanted to save just the owners of these black eyes, but we were at a loss to know what to do. The young owls were only three weeks old and quite unable to manage on their own. I might try my luck as their step-mother for a while, but it had been my experience that wild birds like these, if brought up artificially, easily become dependent on human aid for the rest of their lives and I wanted to save these owlets from such a sad fate.

We had to take a chance that the owl family would refrain from attacking people. In two weeks the young ones would be able to leave the nest and climb around in the trees, and by then the belligerence of the parents would have vanished.

Next day I had trouble staying awake in school. I had slept badly the night before, trying in vain to get the owls off my mind. During the lunch hour I had a telephone call that woke me up! It was from the treasurer of the county hall.

This tawny owl's nest was found in the trunk of an old, hollow elm tree.

The owl doesn't make real nests and the eggs are placed on some rotten pieces of wood. The female prefers a hollow tree, but an old crow's nest will do, or she may pick a suitable corner in a shed or similar outhouse. Like all owl's eggs these are white and round almost like balls. Some scientists maintain that the tawny owl prepares the surface on which the eggs are to be laid, and which is often ice cold, by drying and warming it beforehand.

The tawny owl has excellent eyesight, which is particularly useful in very faint light. It is a typical night owl. The eyes are large and brownish black and are rigidly attached to the eye-sockets, making it necessary for the owl to turn its head to look sideways. The bird in this picture squints a little against the light, but it is far from helpless in daylight. If frightened it will fly even in bright sunlight, although its ability to estimate distances may then be impaired.

'Hafslund, one of the avenue owls sends its regards. It is perched on my curtain rod and seems rather hungry.'

'What – there is an owl in your office?'

'Yes. It got here accidentally. I opened the door of the fireplace to knock the ashes off my pipe, and the owl practically flew into my face. It must have fallen down the chimney.'

Like all other owls the tawny owl has very strong feet with big sharp and curved talons, its chief instrument for hunting its prey.

The tawny owl has incredibly acute hearing. The ear opening is usually completely hidden by the 'veil', the ring of feathers radiating around the eye. It is covered by a skin flap, here folded away to show a little of the ear passage.

I thanked him profusely for the message and promised to have the owl picked up in no time. I couldn't get off myself, but my friend Simon, a hunter and owl expert, took care of the matter.

We had been luckier than we had dared to hope. The day before we had given up the whole evacuation because one of the adult owls was missing, and now one of them was sitting waiting for us. Before nightfall it was in safe custody in my home with its three young ones.

I wondered if we had the father or mother owl. The male and female are identical in appearance, and although the female is slightly larger, the difference is so small that one has to see both simultaneously to decide which is which.

Owls have binocular eyesight, that is their eyes look straight ahead and catch sight of an object simultaneously. If an owl wants to regard something at close quarters, however, it has to turn its head and use one eye at a time. The owl blinks its upper eyelid, just like a human being.

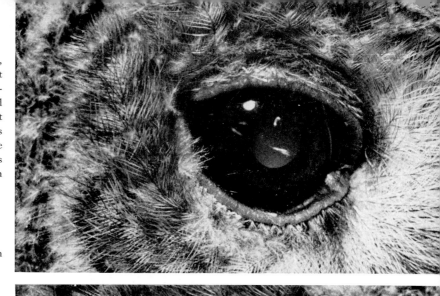

Open eye of a tawny owl seen in close-up.

The owl starts blinking. A white membrane – the blinking membrane – is drawn across the eye-ball before the upper eyelid is lowered. Some zoologists think that it can fly with the membrane drawn.

The eye is closed. Notice the pronounced 'veil'.

The first evening they all stayed in a corner of the room which my eldest son had to give up for the time being. The adult owl showed no inclination to care for the youngsters. Its fear of the new and unknown surroundings was probably too great. But next day the situation was quite idyllic. The adult was shielding the youngsters under its wings, so we evidently had Mama Owl with us.

We fed the owlets liver and chopped whale meat. I put the food in front of the mother and made my departure quickly, as I didn't want them to become too familiar. But, alas, within a week all the youngsters would eat out of my hand, and even the mother sat on it.

When I had had the owls with me a couple of weeks I had an experience which rather frightened me. One day I found one of the owlets lying flat on its belly on a branch of the 'apple tree' which I had rigged up for them. Its wings were hanging down and the tail pointed straight up. What could the matter be? Was there anything wrong with the food I had been giving them? Were the youngsters actually about to die?

I went to Simon who put my mind at rest. The explanation was very simple. When they are four or five weeks old the youngsters leave the nest for good. From then on they rest and sleep in the tree tops, and there they often assume such peculiar positions and attitudes.

The days went by and my guests thrived – but not I. The owls were no longer wild. If the experiment was to end well I had to find a new place for them to stay. Simon suggested giving the owls their freedom at a place far away from people. They were therefore placed in a large cage for transportation, but the night before our departure the door of the cage opened by accident – and the mother owl flew away through the open window. We waited several days, but she didn't return. Then Simon suggested that we set one of the owlets free somewhere near their annual nest in the avenue, as the father

An adult tawny owl in a pitiful condition. It had suffered the fate described in the story – the thrushes had attacked it in daylight, bombarding it with excretions which 'cemented' the feathers together. This owl was quite helpless when it was brought to me, and would undoubtedly have starved to death if it hadn't been found and been given a thorough scrubbing with soap and water all over. As soon as its feathers were clean and dry, the owl could take to its wings again.

owl at least had returned there by now. We went there, and Simon took the young owl and threw it into the air. It flew fairly well, but at once sought the safety of the high grass along a hedge. Here it would be snug and secure until dark – we thought.

Next morning our mutual friend Bodvar was on the telephone to scold me in no uncertain terms. A fine zoologist I was (said he), who didn't understand that thrushes could kill an owlet by bombarding it with their excretions! That's what had happened he told me. But how did he know of the young bird? Oh, Simon had called him to tell of our experiment, mentioning that the thrushes had been jumping around excitedly when we left, and Bodvar had suspected that something might go wrong.

So Bodvar had driven out to the avenue, where, sure enough he found a completely helpless owlet. It couldn't even lift its wings, as the thrushes had 'cemented' it with their droppings. I asked him to bring the bird to me right away, and as soon as he arrived we took the hapless little creature down to the basement and gave it a thorough scrubbing. It was safe for now, but I felt very embarrassed and ashamed.

If we were to save the young owls we had to act quickly. We rang a farmer friend who had an empty shed, and he agreed to let us put the owlets there. In the afternoon of the very same day they were installed in their new home.

I visited the 'emigrants' frequently and saw to my joy that although they ate the food I bought for them, they were becoming increasingly cautious and wild. One day at the beginning of July I left the door of the shed open when I went home. When I arrived for my next visit the birds had flown away. All that was left was some regurgitated pellets – a last greeting thanking me for my hospitality.

THE TAWNY OWL *(Strix aluco)* belongs to a family of owls (Strigidae) with over twenty different species, which are found practically the world over. It attains a length of fourteen to eighteen inches, with a wing length of eleven to twelve inches.
Hatching may start as early as the end of February. There are from two to six eggs in a clutch and the incubation period is twentyeight to thirty days. The owlets leave the nest after a month and can fly when they are five or six weeks old.
The tawny owl lives mostly off small rodents, but eats frogs, small birds and insects as well.

Five-week old tawny owlets.

The Paper Makers

If one looks up the word Paper in an encyclopaedia, one is likely to read that the invention of this precious material can be traced to the Chinese official Ts'ai Lun, who in the year 105 A.D. managed to make paper from rags, fishing nets, hemp and the bark of the mulberry tree.

To be quite fair, however, one should add that Ts'ai Lun only invented 'more paper'. The material had already been in use for millions of years before his time. The wasp is the real pioneer – but it doesn't know it.

Anybody doubting the truth of this statement can safely turn to some scientist or research worker in the paper industry, who will be able to confirm that the material of the wasp nest consists of either cellulose or pulp, according to the type of wasp in question, materials produced in the paper industry.

To most people a wasp is a wasp and that's that. Those who know more about them often distinguish between 'air wasps' and 'ground wasps'. Although I can't really accept this extremely simplified and unscientific distinction, I have been forced to use it in the following story, as the subject of wasps is so huge and so complicated that a whole book could be devoted to it.

There are many types of wasps in our latitudes – burrowing wasps, parasite wasps, wood wasps, leaf wasps, gall-flies and ordinary wasps. Most people know the ordinary wasp, which is the species we will talk about here. All seven varieties of this species existing in Norway belong to the family *Vespa*. Among these the big *Vespa crabro* is easily recognizable as it is nearly twice the size of the other species

17

A meeting at the 'gate': One 'ground wasp' on its way out with a lump of earth, another coming in to land.

Wasp queen in hibernating position. The wings are tucked in under her belly, and the legs and feelers close to the body. This queen was found between the pages of an old newspaper.

The hibernation period lasts several months. Midway through it the queen is so numb and insensitive that she can be handled roughly without awakening her. Here a queen has awakened quite naturally, and after a slow start she is soon full of energy. On the first sunny day she will fly into the open air.

in the family. Its enormously long feelers have given this wasp various popular names.

Everyone knows the wasp's nest, at least on the outside. But many may have wondered how it is constructed and how its interior looks. The building process is actually one of the wonders of nature – simple and ingenious.

The wasp society, which exists for a year at a time, is established when a fertilized female, the queen, survives the winter and awakens once more in spring. One sunny day she starts looking for a suitable

18

place for the nest. Once she has found it she attaches there a triangular piece of 'paper' which is to form the basis for the nest. A strip of paper, twisted to 180°, is glued to the base, and this strip forms a beam, to which the queen attaches the first cells.

As soon as these first cells have been constructed the queen lays her eggs in them. She is incredibly busy, as the building must go on all the time. Raw material is easily found as rotten woodwork is abundant everywhere. With her jaws she crumbles the wood into a mass, which by means of enzymes in her saliva is transformed into the finest cellulose. These enzymes are quite unique in that they act equally well whether the mass is made from deciduous or coniferous wood. Chemicals like that would be the envy of the paper industry.

The nest grows rapidly. The first walls are formed like an umbrella

The queens are the only individuals of the wasp community that survive, and among them only those fertilized hibernate. The other females and all the males or drones die before winter comes. The wasp queen starts building her society as soon as she emerges from her hibernation period. First she searches for a suitable place for her nest, which has to be built painstakingly from scratch. If she is a 'ground wasp' she finds a building site in the ground – in a meadow, a lawn or maybe in the heather of the moor – but she may also find a place where the nest can more easily be placed, for instance in an attic, between the panels of a wooden building, or underneath the roof tiles. The 'air wasp' makes do with just about anything as long as the nest can be attached to it, – usually high in the tree tops, between the branches of dense bushes or in sheltered corners of old out-houses.

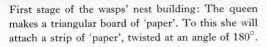
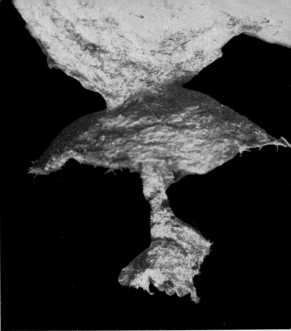

First stage of the wasps' nest building: The queen makes a triangular board of 'paper'. To this she will attach a strip of 'paper', twisted at an angle of 180°.

The paper strip becomes a beam, and the first cell comb is attached to that. The first wall layer now begins to form, like an umbrella.

under the attachment, and gradually the construction assumes ball form. Within the nest the cells are placed in layers, just like stories in a house. The cells are not usually attached to the walls, but are connected by vertical paper beams.

To make room for an increasing number of wasps the queen has to extend the nest all the time. This is done in the brilliantly simple way of tearing down the walls, which are erected one outside the other, from within. This material is used over and over again for new wall layers.

The walls of a nest of 'air wasps' like the one described are very much exposed to weather and temperature changes, and therefore have to be of the very best quality.

The 'ground wasp' doesn't make its nest out of such high quality materials. As its nest is so well protected, it is content to use pulp.

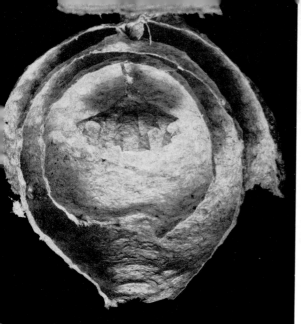

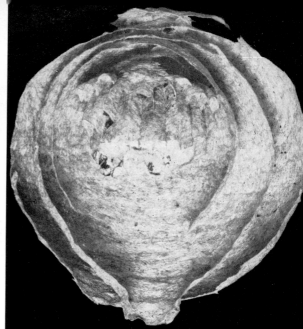

Walls are formed, layer by layer. In this unfinished nest which has been cut through, the first cell comb can be glimpsed in the middle.

As the cell combs grow the nest must be expanded. So the innermost walls have to go down, and the material from them is used for new outer walls!

Finished wasps' nest in a juniper bush. This is a typical 'air wasp' nest. The walls are made of cellulose, produced from plant fibres by the wasp itself, and of a very high quality. A nest like this one isn't finished until fairly late in summer, when the community descending from the single queen has produced hundreds of busy workers. Inside the nest are usually three or four cell combs, placed on top of each other like stories in a house. They are as a rule not attached to the walls, but the top one is connected to the roof and between them there are strong, vertical paper beams.

A special feature of this nest is the presence of two openings – the main entrance at the bottom and an emergency entrance or exit a little higher. These nests are rarely found.

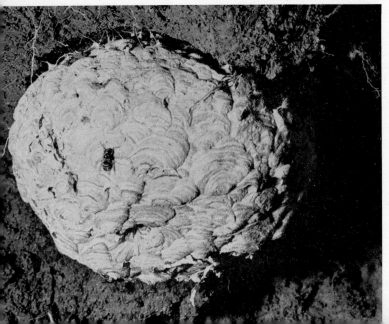

△ When uncovering a 'ground wasp' nest, it pays to be well protected.

◁ The 'ground wasp' nest is laid open. The approach to this nest, thirteen inches across, was through a seventeen-inch-long tunnel entrance (its opening is seen on the colour plate facing page 17). The nest was freely suspended inside a larger cave, with a clearance of three-eighths of an inch all around the nest. The walls of an underground nest like this are made of pulp and have a different structure from the walls of the 'air wasp' nest. They are better protected against adverse weather, and can be made of coarser material.

Not long ago I asked a scientist doing research in the paper industry to analyze the material from the wall of a 'ground wasp' nest, and he found that it was mainly made of a mechanically produced mass from deciduous wood. The wasps had crushed the wood into tiny splinters and cemented them with saliva.

In the interior of the nest new and strange things are constantly happening. The first new wasps appear as complete insects about three weeks after the first eggs were laid. Throughout the spring and summer only sterile female offspring are born. These female workers are doomed to a life in slavery. They do nothing but build, provide food and feed younger brothers and sisters.

Toward the end of the summer there is no need for more workers. Then the queen starts producing fertile males (drones) and females (queens) which leave the nest as soon as they are fully developed, to mate. When winter comes the impregnated queens, at least some of them, have found shelter for hibernating. The males all die, but a new generation of wasps is ensured.

'Air wasp' hard at work building a wall. A piece of wood has been brought in from outside, and with its powerful jaws the wasp chews the piece into a moist mass, forming it into an elongated 'sausage' which is stretched along the edge of the wall to be extended. The wasp moves backward while working, and the sausage is worked over three times in all before the wasp is finished.

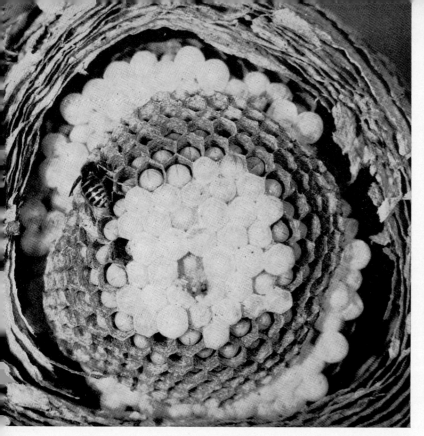

Cross section of a three storey nest. This is the *bottom* storey. The middle cells were each covered by a white cupola, containing wasps in the pupal stage. The open cells contained wasp larvae.

The *middle* floor of the nes were eggs and tiny larvae. but only one in each cell wi

In the nest only the workers and the old queen remain, and the end is rapidly approaching. The food supply steadily decreases, and one day the queen leaves her nest for good, seeking death outside. Toward the end panic reigns in the nest. The adult wasps either devour or expel the younger ones, and soon there are only a few individuals left. They die when frost comes and the bustling society is tranformed into an empty ruin.

If I now dwell on the 'ground wasps', it is not because life in their community is any different from other species. The reason is that recently I discovered something strange about these wasps.

24

en cells of the comb there
contained several larvae,
ed.

Top floor of the nest. Here were wasps in all stages of development – eggs, larvae, pupae. This was the oldest cell comb of the nest, attached directly to the ceiling.

My good friend Karsten, a very alert and experienced naturalist, one day found a tunnel leading into a 'ground wasp' nest, but the opening was so narrow that this couldn't possibly be the entrance to an old mouse nest. And didn't the 'ground wasp' take over old mouse corridors? That's what the books said.

Karsten dashed home and got himself a big knife. He cut into the ground and about sixteen inches from the surface the narrow path ended in a small, spherical room. From its roof there was a small, orange ball hanging – the nest. It was three inches in diameter and the room around it barely four inches.

Karsten immediately saw that it was a 'ground wasp' nest. 'How could this nest be made bigger?' he asked himself. An ordinary nest in the ground was usually some sixteen inches in diameter. Karsten began to doubt the mouse corridor theory. He telephoned me and asked me to join him.

I had to agree with him. This could not be a mouse nest corridor or natural hollow in the ground, where the books said 'ground wasps' usually nested. Did the wasps themselves really act as bulldozers?

Later that summer we had the answer. We had discovered another nesting place for 'ground wasps'. The opening leading to the underground room was so narrow that even the wasps had very little space. We marked the place well and agreed to visit it often.

Then, as so often happens, we became too busy with other things. Not until late September did we have the time to go there again. But what a surprise we got! The tunnel in the ground was by now as wide as a mouse passage, the clover around it was cut down, and there were wasps galore.

The thoughtful Karsten had brought full equipment, and he lost no time getting into his wasp-proof suit. Using his big knife he started

The micro-photographs below show the structure of the nest walls of the 'air wasp' (left) and 'ground wasp'. One can clearly see how the first has made cellulose from clean, whole plant fibres, by means of enzymes in the 'air wasp' saliva. The 'ground wasp' doesn't need such fine material. It produces pulp, which is nothing but coarse chips cemented together with saliva.

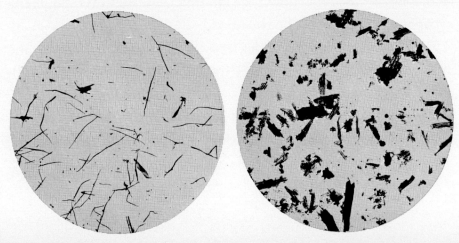

Worker wasp feeding a larva. During the first days after they are hatched the larvae are fed floral honey (nectar), but this is soon insufficient. The queen and the other adults have to get animal food, for instance flies, for the larvae. At an early age the workers have to share the burden of feeding younger brothers and sisters. Later on they have to go on foraging trips to supply the community.

to lay open the nest. I kept at a safe distance, as I had no equipment with me other than my photographic gear, which is not much use against ill-tempered wasps.

Karsten beckoned to me, and when I was at close quarters I saw one wasp after the other appear in the opening, most of them with a big lump of earth between their jaws.

Here we had conclusive proof. I told Karsten to go on digging, but he had not carried on for many seconds when hundreds of wasps went into a raging attack. He worked calmly on in his wasp-proof suit, and in a little while the attack subsided and I was able to venture closer once more.

Soon Karsten disclosed part of the nest. The building material and construction were unmistakable. This was an ordinary 'ground wasp' nest.

It was now so late that we had to stop working for the day. But we couldn't leave the nest open, or we might risk a badger taking the whole thing. We covered the spot with pine branches, putting some big, heavy ones on top.

When we came back the next morning and removed the twigs and branches we found that the square opening which Karsten had made, was now closed. This was not so remarkable, but the astonishing thing was that the wasps had cemented the opening using earth and saliva! Where there had been an opening, there was now a square section, much lighter in colour than the soil around it. It looked like dry clay.

We had assumed that the wasps would close up the opening with pulp, the same kind they use for the walls of their nests, but they must have rejected this material as too weak and brittle. This was a new discovery to us, and eagerly we started to disclose the whole nest. Right away masses of wasps swarmed forth. Their community was still intact.

The nest was round like a ball, some seventeen inches in diameter. The chamber around it was exactly three-eighths of an inch wider all around, in other words spherical too.

We got our greatest surprise when we investigated how the nest was suspended in this underground chamber. It was attached to the roof by means of several beams, and these beams were made of light, firm earth, as hard as concrete!

Full-grown larvae fill their cells completely. They hang head downwards and stay in place solely because of their own bulk. At this stage a lot of reserve nourishment has been stored in the larva's body. These supplies will come in handy from now on, because the carefree eating days are over. The time of transformation draws near.

In the bottom of the round room around the nest there was a fairly deep depression where we found distinct markings of the wasps' powerful jaws. It was from here that the earth was removed and transported into the open – we had seen scores of wasps flying out with earth lumps between their jaws.

△ Before the transformation can start the larva must spin a lid to cover its cell. It is made of fine silk thread, produced by the larva's spinning glands. Here are shown three finished lids and one under construction. Inside the lid – in the cell – the larva spins its silk cocoon. It is very thin and sticks closely to the lid and walls of the cell. All this work is finished by the larva in less than a day.

◁ Detail showing the fine silk thread in the lid of the cell. It takes from eight to nine hours to finish spinning the lid.

Wasp pupae shortly before appearing as insects. The dark one is five days ahead in its development. The real transformation has already taken place in the so-called pre-pupal stage – the period after the larva made its cocoon and before the pupa appeared. The pupal period is really only a maturing period. The pupa is on the whole just like a finished insect, apart from the colours. Antennae, legs and wings are held close to the body, like a wasp hibernating. The wings are just small, deflated bags as yet, however. They will be inflated when the finished insect is hatched.

After a few days the skin of the pupa gets its colours. The process starts with the eyes and goes on to the rest of the head, then to the chest and the hind part of the body. The dark pupa in this picture is closer to finished colouration. What makes it appear dark (actually blue) is a thin skin covering it completely. Beneath this skin it is black and yellow, just like a mature, fully grown wasp. When the finished wasp is about to be hatched, it starts gnawing through the lid of its cell. It moistens the silk capsule with saliva, and in five or six hours it is through and in the open.

I couldn't then explain the purpose of this depression, but later that autumn, after we had placed the nest in a birch tree near Karsten's home, it dawned on me. By now the whole community was doomed anyway, so we had no qualms about cutting up the nest to study the cell combs at closer quarters and in detail.

We found no queen cells on the ground floor, only workers' cells. The queen cells are nearly half again as wide as the workers' cells and are always placed in the lowest cell comb, so there was no chance of being mistaken. When we took the cells apart we found the old queen.

Suddenly the whole thing was brilliantly clear to me: The workers had of course started the foundations for the last phase of the construction work, but when Karsten and I dug out the nest and moved it, they had closed down their work, and thus this community had no new queens.

WASPS belong to the order Hymenoptera. With more than 100,000 known species, this order is the third largest among insects (next to beetles and butterflies). Wasps' wings are short and narrow, resembling oarblades, the rear wings much shorter than the front pair. At the front edge of the rear wings are hooks which can be attached to a fold in the rear of the front wings, enabling the wasp to connect the wing pairs during flight. Another typical feature is the longitudinal folding of the wings during rest.
The wasp has distinctive colouring in the form of black and yellow rings around the hind part of the body.

The finished insect is on its way out. Its antennae are pointed forward – the sensory organs function!

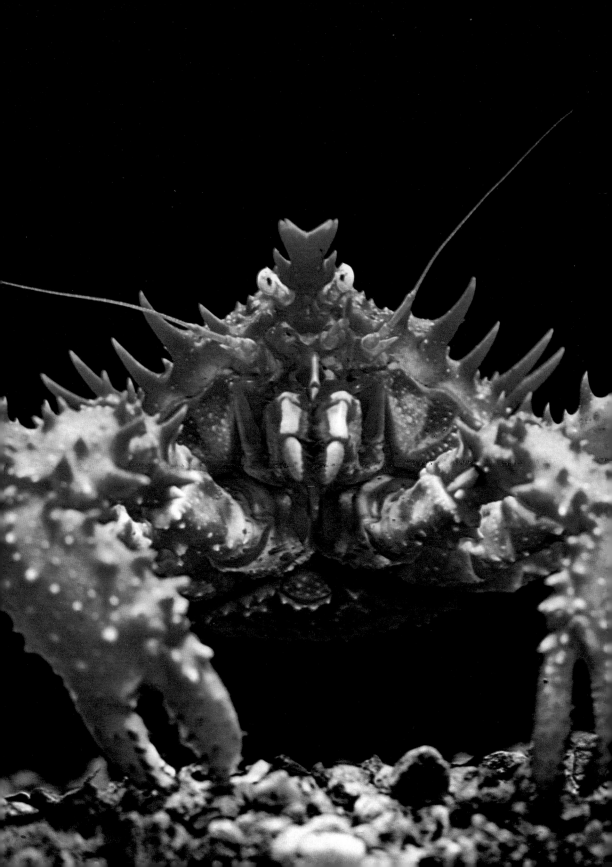

In Shallow and Deep Water

It has now become increasingly popular to buy some underwater swimming gear and start out as an amateur diver. Apart from the dangers of indiscrimate diving with unsuitable equipment this is a development I welcome. For holiday makers along the coast, a hitherto almost unknown world has been opened up. There is a vivid interest in that which moves underneath the surface, whether on the beach or in deeper water. To stimulate this interest I should like to show you a glimpse of the rich life which abounds on our shores.

One of the first creatures one meets is the small shore crab. It is so well known that I will not waste many words on it. As a small boy I believed that the small crab eventually would grow to be as big and heavy as the edible crab, but today most children know that the shore crab will always remain small. No matter how old it gets to be, it rarely measures more than four inches across.

But the big edible crab is a different matter altogether. It can be as much as twelve inches across, and some that have been caught have weighed as much as fifteen pounds. Late in summer one sometimes encounters an edible crab close in to the beach, but most of the year it stays in deeper water. When it comes in to shallow water, it gorges itself on clams and mussels, but if you expect to find the crab full of meat at this time, you will probably be disappointed. Crabs have to change their shell to increase in size, as the shell itself does not grow.

Just after changing the shell the crab has a very soft, new skin and until this has become a hard armour through calcification, the

33

tone crab in a close-up.

Shore crabs mating. The mating takes place in midsummer shortly after the female has changed its shell.

THE SHORE CRAB *(Carcinus maenas)* is found in shallow waters along the North Atlantic coast. In the winter it goes down to greater depths. It lives mainly off dead animals, and its dorsal shield can be up to four inches wide and three inches long.

THE EDIBLE CRAB *(Cancer pagurus)* measures up to twelve inches across the shield and can weigh as much as fifteen pounds. It stays mainly on clay or rock bottom in very salty water.
The dorsal shield is nearly oval and reddish brown on top. Underneath the crab is lighter in colour. The scissor prongs of the claws are black-purple toward the tips. They are very powerful and can flatten an unwary finger quite effectively.

crab has to remain hidden and to do without food. So even if it has stuffed itself with mussels for a while after leaving its hiding place, it has a lot to catch up with after the long fast.

The reproduction of the crab is a fascinating chapter in itself. After the male seed has been transferred to the female ovaries, the opening in the female's body through which the seed passes is closed by a layer of mucus which then hardens. The eggs in the female body do not mature until a year later, and not until then can they be fertilized by the seed which has been kept alive within the female oviducts since mating the year before. Fertilization takes place in the oviducts as the eggs are pressed outwards to their 'anchoring place' underneath the tail. Later the female carries 'out-roe' for more than six months, the eggs being hatched some twenty-one months after mating takes place.

The big edible crab, a well-known delicacy, is the biggest crab in Europe. It stays mostly at a depth of from thirty to one hundred feet, but in summer it sometimes appears quite close to shore.

The spider crab has a triangular dorsal shield which makes it easy to distinguish it from other crabs.

The spider crab moves very slowly at the bottom. It is a master in the art of camouflage, using small bits of plants which it cuts off with its claws and then fastens to small hooks on its shell. This makes it very hard to see the crab.

The spider crab is not widely known, but this curious creature deserves to be mentioned. It has long, sensitive and mobile claws which it uses to cut algae and water plants into small pieces, moving them bit by bit via its mouth to the dorsal shield which is full of tiny hooks. This is the only type of crab with such flexible claws. The shore crab and the edible crab can only move their claws as far as their mouths.

Many wonder why the spider crab uses such a strange camouflaging device, decorating itself until it is almost invisible when resting at the bottom. It moves slowly and as little as possible, and its grip is not very strong. Perhaps that is why it needs to pass unnoticed.

Fishermen just hate to get spider crabs in their nets. Their long legs get entangled in the mesh and they can cause a great deal of damage when they cut the thread to extricate themselves. They don't use their scissor-claws but their powerful jaws, clearly seen in the picture on the right. In the left picture the tail of the spider crab has been folded out and the 'out-roe' laid open.

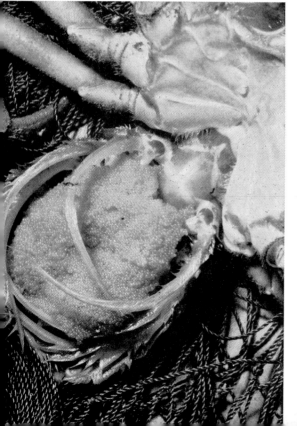

I have often found spider crabs in my nets. It is no joke, for the long arms of these small crabs get entangled in the mesh. To disengage themselves the crabs chew away at the net with their powerful jaws and can cause great damage. Nylon nets are especially prone to destruction. It seems that crabs' saliva dissolves nylon fibres, and the nets are quite rotten where the crabs have been.

In recent years many people have become familiar with Russian and Japanese crab-meat, available in tins in almost any grocery store. But not very many know that the same delicacy abounds in our own waters, at least in the shape of a very close but much smaller relative – the stone crab.

The name is misleading, for this is really not a crab at all. It has only four pair of legs, while proper crabs possess five. The pair of extremities which corresponds to the hind legs of crabs, is tiny and hidden in the gill cavity. In other ways, too, the stone crab is peculiar. Its tail has not been deflected into a depression on the belly side, but flattened against it – obliquely. It contains the liver, among other things, but in real crabs the liver is found in the body itself, under the dorsal shield.

△ The hermit-crab has no hard shell on its hind-body. This part must be well protected against greedy beasts of prey, and so the hermit-crab seeks refuge in empty snail-shells. As long as it is quite small, it uses the shells of beach-snails, but when it grows older and lives in deeper water it takes up residence in a shell of a larger snail like the one here *(Buccinum undatum)*. If the new house which it wants happens to be occupied, this is no deterrent. Often the hermit-crab hauls a live snail out of its shell and eats it piece by piece until the shell is vacant. And then the vulnerable hind-quarters go out of the old abode and into the new one which was reluctantly evacuated by the snail.

▷ The asymmetric tail of the stone crab (see next page). This animal is related to the hermit-crab, but neither is really a crab, in spite of the name.

The stone crab is thus no crab at all. It is a hermit-crab – without a place to stay. The ordinary hermit-crab has to find shelter and protection for its soft, unprotected hind-quarters in a snail-shell, but the stone crab with its armoured tail can do without a house.

he Japanese and the Russian crabs.

THE (NORTHERN) STONE CRAB *(Lithodes maia)* is related to the hermit crab, although it looks more like an ordinary crab. It is quite common along the entire Norwegian coast at depths of a hundred to three hundred feet, often on a rocky bottom amidst deep-growing red algae. The dorsal shield can be as much as six inches in length and width, and the legs nearly fourteen inches long. Both are equipped with big thorns.

In places where the water is very salty and there is a strong current, one can find some strange animals – which not only compete with the loveliest flowers in shape and colours, but even have plant names. They are the beautiful sea-anemones. In spite of their exotic appearance they are far more common than one assumes, and are often found close to the shore.

Here is an experiment which I performed with one such animal, a plumose anemone. I wanted to move it into my aquarium from one of the dock-pillars belonging to my friend Anton, a fisherman who has helped me many times. But moving such a creature is no simple matter. There has to be – above all – new, salty water in the aquarium, water that moves, or the plumose anemone contracts and refuses to co-operate.

The anemone was so firmly attached to the pillar that it was impossible to pry it loose. I had to have it in one piece, so there was no choice but to attack the woodwork with hammer and chisel. The anemone reacted to the first stroke, contracting completely, and it was like a lifeless lump for several hours after it had been moved into the aquarium.

The plumose anemone looks like a flower, but it is really an active animal, moving from place to place. The nearest illustration shows the plumose anemone 'in flower' – in the centre picture some irritation has caused it to draw the tentacles into its stomach cavity – while in the picture to the right it is completely contracted. Only a long, thin thread with poisonous cells protrudes and protects the animal against surprise attacks.

Late that night something finally happened — and a lovely and grand spectacle it was. Slowly thousands of 'petals' appeared from the inside of the animal, stretching outward into the water. In a few minutes the whole top of the animal was like a big, splendid flower.

The plumose anemone had obviously got used to its new home already, for after a while it started fishing. Its tentacles swayed rhythmically back and forth in the current, curving in toward the mouth and then stretching slowly again.

The tentacles of the plumose anemone are densely covered with fine ciliae and a great number of nettle cells. When another animal touches the cells, these 'explode' and their poison paralyzes the victim. In the middle of the circle of tentacles is the mouth, which receives the prey by means of the movements of the water.

THE PLUMOSE ANEMONE *(Metridium senile)* belongs to the Sea Anemones of the animal group nettles comprising about 9,000 known species. It is found along the entire Norwegian coast down to depths of a hundred feet, and can attain a height of eight inches.

A small fish has been caught by a beadlet anemone near the shore. Thousands of tiny hooks on the tentacles holds the victim, while poison cells paralyze it completely. It is then moved into the sea anemone's mouth and on to the stomach where it is devoured.

THE BEADLET ANEMONE *(Actinia equina)* likes especially shallow water with a strong current. Found along the Norwegian coast from Stavanger to the North Cape, it is two inches high with a 'crown' some two and a half inches wide.

THE DEEP WATER ANEMONE *(Bolocera tuediae)* can be found along the whole Norwegian coast at depths of sixty to a thousand feet. This sea anemone can be as much as twelve inches high and ten inches across, and is usually salmon-coloured, sometimes dark red. It is the giant among our sea anemones.

A deep water anemone has caught itself a shrimp. In a couple of days it will expel the empty shell.

The ordinary starfish lives in shallow water. It seems quite lifeless and harmless, but it is really a voracious beast of prey. The splendid specimen above was born with only four arms. The arms or tentacles are covered underneath with suction cups or feet (right). The mouth is quite small, so victims that are too big to be swallowed in one piece, receive special treatment.

It may seem unbelievable that the ordinary starfish is an unusually greedy preying animal. 'What,' you may think, 'can a flat, lifeless thing like that do?'

Oh yes, the starfish is a killer, all right. It doesn't use conventional weapons like claws, talons, teeth, beak or poisonous sting to do away with its prey. It kills with its stomach!

To explain this peculiar behaviour let me tell you how a starfish attacks a mussel and finishes it off.

Mussels seem to be the starfish's favourite food, but how can it cope with such a well-protected animal?

It begins as a tug-of-war. Five arms or tentacles – with altogether some thousand suction feet – try to pull the two shells apart, while

46

When a starfish prepares to eat a bigger animal it turns its stomach inside out through its small mouth and starts its digestive process outside its own body. The food is then sucked into the body along with the stomach! This is so big that it almost covers the starfish's arms when it has been fully extended. Here a starfish has been brutally removed from its favourite dish, a mussel, and its stomach is not yet completely in place.

the starfish is firmly astride the mussel. The assaulted party holds back with everything it has got, using transverse muscles in its body, pulling the shells together. These muscles are much more powerful than anything the starfish can muster.

Yet the outcome is a foregone conclusion. The mussel must lose. This is not because it tires more easily. On the contrary, its contracting muscles 'rest' while they pull. No, a flanking movement is needed, and it will come, surely and unmercifully.

The two mussel shells don't fit together quite closely all the way round. On one side, opposite the 'lock', there is a small crack, through which the mussel foot can protrude, and this is where the starfish launches its stomach attack.

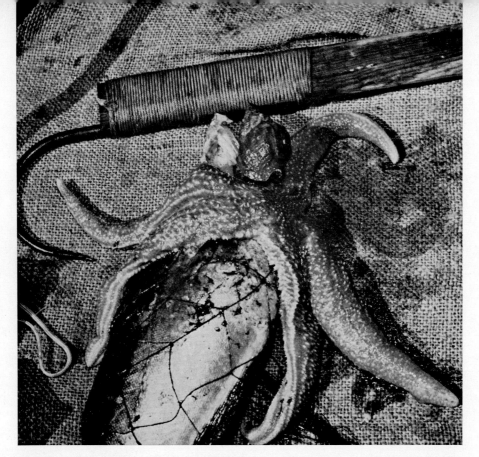

This picture shows how greedy the starfish really is. A cod-fish was caught in the net, but before the fisherman hauled it in, a starfish had eaten half the head. Its stomach acid is strong enough to dissolve bone substance and chalk.

The starfish doesn't need much of an opening, as long as it is big enough to enable part of its stomach to intrude into the mussel shell and produce sufficient amounts of stomach acid. This acid paralyzes the muscles of the mussel – and suddenly the shells come apart. Like a plate the open mussel displays its delicious meat – for the starfish to devour at leisure.

The starfish presses its stomach all over the victim so that the entire mussel inside the shell is completely covered. The water is pushed aside and the meat can be devoured undiluted by sea water. When

48

A plumose anemone 'in full flower'.

the 'plate' is empty the starfish pulls in its stomach and takes its leave.

Taking its leave sounds very simple. But we know very little about the habits and means of locomotion of the starfish.

The starfish has no definite front part of its body. Any one of the five tentacles can act independently as a front extremity, as there are feelers and tiny, primitive eyes on each. The eyes are so simple that they merely give the animal an indication of light and shadows in its surroundings. They cannot form any pictorial impressions, and so the starfish strictly speaking cannot see. It must therefore be the senses of smell and taste which direct the animal's behaviour. If it moves in a definite direction it is led by smell, taste and feeling. The arm-point, or 'head' which reacts the strongest, directs the animal.

THE COMMON STARFISH *(Asterias rubens)* is one of the commonest animals of the beach, but it is also found in quite deep water, as much as 700 feet below the surface. It belongs to the *echinoderms* group. Starfish frequently lose one or more tentacles in the struggle for survival, but they have a phenomenal regenerative capacity, and the lost limb is soon replaced. Starfish measuring eight inches across are often found in shallow water, but specimens taken from the depths may be considerably bigger. The starfish is a greedy beast of prey and eats snails, mussels, worms and fish caught in nets.

Starfish eating a mussel.

Ex-Rodent

When I told Simon that he must no longer think of the hare as a rodent, he wasn't quite as surprised as I had expected. He did think it strange that something he had been taught in childhood should be wrong, but on the other hand he had often wondered if the hare might not be related to the kangaroo. He had often heard that in Greenland and some other places there were hares jumping around only on their hind legs.

Hare in late winter suit.

The hare's most characteristic features are its long ears and the pronounced difference between long, powerful hind legs and short, thin forelegs. The hare most commonly found in Norway is white in wintertime, apart from the tips of its ears, which remain black all year round. In summer the main colour is greyish brown. In some districts the hare is grey-blue, not white, in winter. Zoologists distinguish between the two types of Nordic hare: the white mountain hare *(Lepus timidus borealis)* and the grey-blue hare of the plains *(Lepus timidus sylvaticus)*.

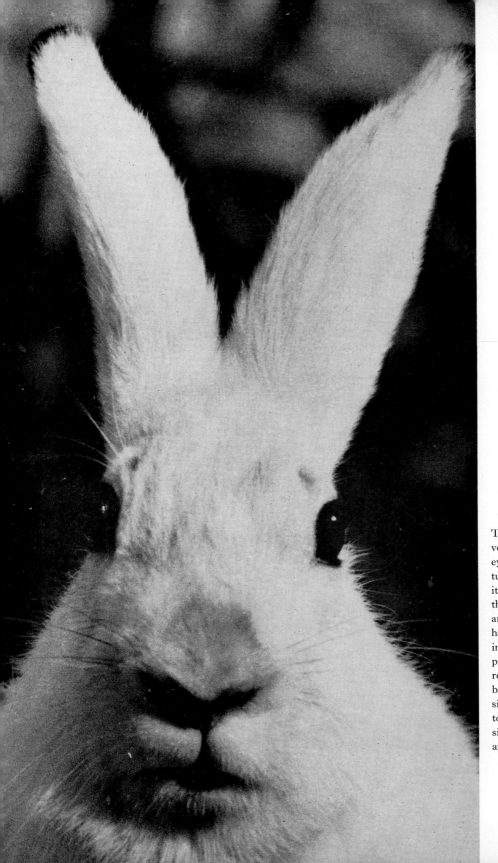

This picture shows very clearly that the eyes of the hare are turned sideways, and it is not strange, therefore, that there are many stories of hares running straight into tree trunks when pursued. Another reason for this may be that the hare's sight is not adjusted to bright daylight, since it is a nocturnal animal.

The hare believes in cleanliness and constantly grooms itself. These pictures give a good impression of the great difference between front and hind leg length. The hare can neither walk nor trot, it is forced to jump, an art which it masters to perfection. When hotly pursued it can made jumps of fifteen to twenty feet, travelling at thirty to thirty-five miles an hour.

No, Simon was ready to accept the fact that the hare is no longer classified as a rodent. But how could our school books be so wrong? Why, even serious books on zoology still had the hare listed as a rodent.

Modern, systematic zoology groups hares and rabbits in a separate order among mammals, different from the rodents. This distinction is of a recent date, but fossilized bones of hares and of real rodents, some sixty million years old, have been found. These fossils, which must date from the very earliest mammals, show as equally distinct variations in important anatomical features as those found between hares and real rodents today. Therefore, if a common original type ever did exist, it must have lived as far back as the earliest reptiles. Simon shook his head in admiration of the brilliance and thoroughness of scientists.

Being an experienced hunter, especially of hares, Simon had encountered quite a few of them. His conclusion was that there was something about the hare's teeth which didn't quite conform with its erstwhile relatives, the rodents. What did I think?

Oh yes, Simon had something there. The hare has indeed two big chisel-shaped front teeth in its upper jaw and two in the lower, but in the upper jaw there are in addition two *small* front teeth, one on each side of the big ones, which rodents don't have. Furthermore, the lower jaw is fastened to the joint in a different way. The hare chews vegetable food almost like the bovine animals – moving jaws and molars from side to side.

THE COMMON EUROPEAN HARE *(Lepus europaeus)* is not found in its wild state in my homeland, but the smaller type *(Lepus timidus)* is found all over Norway. The length of the body is twenty to twenty-four inches and the tail two to two and a half inches. The ears reach the tip of its nose when they are folded forward.

Bulldozer
and Swimming Champion

Some years ago I thought I had been lucky enough to come across an animal unknown in Scandinavia. A strange little animal had been brought in to the editor of a local newspaper, and they asked me to come and identify the creature.

I found a funny little specimen waiting to be classified. It resembled a rat quite closely, but the fur on its back was soft, bluish black and short-haired. I poked at its teeth. There were two pairs of chisel-shaped front teeth; in other words, this must be a rodent. But none

My albino vole admiring its reflection in the water. Albino mammals are not as rare as many people believe. These animals lack pigment in the skin and hair. Their eyes are red because the iris is colourless, letting the blood colour show through. Albinism is usually accompanied by other defects. This vole had softer fur than usual, and because it was lacking in fat content the fur was not water-repellent, which made the animal wet for some time after immersion in water.

of the rodents I knew had fur like this. Could it have been a stowaway on a ship from abroad? Not unlikely, as it had been found not far from the docks.

As I couldn't decide myself I had to ask the advice of a real expert on small rodents. He told me that it was an old friend, a water-vole or water-rat. But I had met a rather unusual specimen, as this one had the so-called Samson defect. This appears not infrequently in fur-covered farm animals, and sometimes in wild foxes. The outer hair of the back fur is missing, so that the underlying woolly hair is visible.

56

Although the animal itself was no zoological rarity, its defect was nevertheless so marked that the fur eventually ended up in a museum as a prize specimen.

Some time later I had an albino water-vole as a visitor. It was an amusing acquaintance. I gave it plenty of room to play around in, and it made full use of the opportunity. It dug passages in all directions, working as fast as any real bulldozer or excavator. Its front legs worked quickly and efficiently, and it pushed away the surplus earth with its head.

Most of the day it stayed underground, but in the evening it came and sat down to eat with its food between its front legs. I let it have plenty of vegetables. It didn't want any drinking water, but then its food contained all the water necessary.

The water-vole and the so-called field-rat are one and the same animal. In Norway we have now introduced one common name for it, thus trying to avoid the many misunderstandings that have

The vole shows its proficiency in the water. On the surface it swims like a dog, and when diving it is almost as supple and graceful as a seal. It can stay submerged for several minutes. Voles living in the ground stay away from the water, but if need be they are just as nimble and resourceful in the water as the water-voles.

The vole belongs to the hamster group of rodents. In its underground passages it collects plentiful winter supplies, especially potatoes and carrots. Its food consists of plant-stems and roots as well, and in its search for these the vole causes serious damage. Great areas can be afflicted by the forages of voles.

This looks like newly-washed potatoes placed neatly in piles in the earth. It is really part of the winter supply stores accumulated by a vole. There is some confusion regarding this underground activity. The vole is often mistakenly called a mole. Moles are not even rodents, but belong to the insect eaters, along with hedgehogs and shrew mice.

Vole with Samson defect. The fur lacks outer hairs and the woolly under hair is exposed on the back as well as on the sides. With this specimen the defect was so pronounced that to begin with we had difficulty in establishing that it really was a water-vole.

occurred. This vole looks a good deal like a rat, as previously mention-ed, but it definitely has not the strange habits of an ordinary brown rat. If a vole lives as a field-rat, it stays away from the water when possible, but if it has to plunge in it is an excellent swimmer.

THE WATER-VOLE *(Arvicola amphibius)* is also known as field-rat or water-rat. It looks a bit like an ordinary brown rat, but its ears are shorter, the snout more snubbed and the neck relatively shorter. Normally the vole is dark brown. Its tail is furry, while the rat tail is shell-clad with only a few weak hairs.

The vole eats only vegetable food, in the summer mainly grass and small plants, in the winter carrots, potatoes, beets, corn and roots. It is a typical hamster and accumulates large winter stores.

The length of the body is six to eight inches while the tail is four to five inches long. The vole gives birth to several litters in the course of a summer, often five or six youngsters in each.

Almost like a Kangaroo

One of the most difficult photographic jobs I have ever tackled was trying to get clearly visible field mouse tracks in the snow. There is no trick to catching live field mice, but these animals are so nervous that they can barely be handled, particularly when one wants them to behave in a special way. Furthermore they are not fond of snow.

I had some fine specimens and we prepared for the job in a suitable place. The camera was set for a close-up, for the tracks are so tiny. This makes the job particularly difficult, but one can always hope to be lucky.

But I got no pictures that could be used. No sooner was a field mouse dropped on to the snow than he made an enormous jump, then another – and presto! – he was gone. One after the other disappeared this way.

Well, there was nothing to be done about it. I hadn't had much faith in this experiment, anyway, so there was no great damage. And I did get something in return for my efforts. I measured the distance between the marks in the snow and determined that this tiny creature twice had jumped more than thirty-two inches! Not bad indeed – a jump of more than seven times its own body length.

When I got home I looked through all my literature on mice, and was pleased to find that a German zoologist had measured the distances jumped by field mice, and had arrived at about the same figure as I had. It is always reassuring to have one's figures confirmed if they seem unbelievably high. But why unbelievable? The rodent group – in its broadest sense – can boast of some jumping mice which

In southern Norway the field mouse, known locally as the wood mouse, has almost entirely displaced its close relative the house mouse, and is a frequent visitor in homes and cabins.

61

Winter supplies of cherry stones.

These hazel nuts have been worked over by mice teeth, but two different species have been at them. The peculiarly regular cut is caused by the bank vole, while the coarser work on the other nut bears the mark of a field mouse.

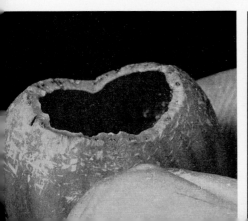

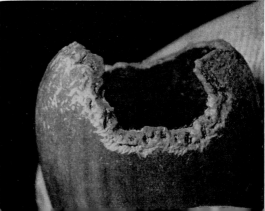

The field mouse is a nocturnal animal, as can be seen by the big eyes.

soar to a distance of ten feet in each jump, not to mention the desert leaping mice which use their long hind legs to get up such a speed that the eye can hardly follow their progress. Among zoologists a hoary joke is still heard: 'Why are the desert mice in such a hurry?' 'Well, their sources of food are so few and far between that they have to go fast, else they would starve to death!'

But the field mouse rarely starves. It often gorges itself on seeds and fruits and collects large supplies in its nest or in very special hiding places. There are many indications that it is a rather intelligent little creature. When its brings home corn it doesn't take one grain at a time, but fills its mouth and brings quite a load each trip. Thus the little animal collects impressive quantities in a short while.

I did not use the name kangaroo as a chapter heading just because the field mouse has long hind legs and can jump very far and high. Even when sitting on its hind legs, leaning on its tail, it does resemble its Australian 'relative'. The tail, which is a good deal longer than the body itself, is an excellent stabilizer for a climbing field mouse. It waves to and fro like a tight-rope walker's pole, and gives the body extra support when needed.

THE FIELD MOUSE *(Apodemus sylvaticus)* is found in southern Norway, where it has almost completely replaced the house mouse *(Mus musculus)*. Its size varies a great deal, and in many countries a distinction is made between two types of field mice – the one mentioned above and the somewhat bigger yellow-necked field-mouse *(Apodemus flavicollis)*.

The field mouse is very fond of nuts, and easily cuts through the hard shell of a hazel nut.

A versatile little Innocent

Graceful, quick, sweet, confident – and many other flattering adjectives might suitably be used to describe the squirrel. But the supple body, the large, limpid eyes, the splendid ear tufts and the lovely furry tail of this rodent charmer can lead us to forget that the squirrel is actually a vicious robber, as many a small bird has learned. I myself have experienced how unfriendly a wild squirrel can be.

I wanted to investigate a special feature of squirrels, and for this experiment I needed a really wild specimen. I set a trap in the woods and caught one without too much trouble. To be on the safe side I had put on mink gloves – don't get me wrong – I mean solid gloves for protection against bites from minks in mink farms!

Nevertheless, when I started to take the squirrel out of the trap, I was surprised. It at once plunged its powerful teeth into my right index finger, biting right through the thick glove, which provides sufficient protection against the blood-thirsty mink, but not against the dapper little squirrel! For several days afterwards I bore the marks of the sharp squirrel teeth. Needless to say, through this blitz attack on my finger the squirrel made its way to freedom. How could the frightened animal know that I was only going to borrow it for a short time?

Scientists who have studied the habits of the squirrel closely, think that it is not very intelligent. But it can be incredibly stubborn and at times it does surprising and inexplicable things.

Some years ago I discovered a new side to the squirrel. My friend Alf and I were out fishing in a rubber boat on a small mountain lake, some 3,000 feet above sea level. Alf weighs some 220 pounds, and

Swimming squirrels are not commonly found, even by those who often walk in the woods. Experiments have proved that the squirrel can't manage very well in cold water. Its fur is not water-repellent, and the belly fur particularly is so sparse that the squirrel easily gets stiff and cold.

our rubber boat was deep in the water. The weather was perfect, sunny, warm and quiet, and we were dozing peacefully.

Suddenly Alf started, pointed towards land and said in a loud voice:

'Look, isn't that an otter in the water there?'

Yes, it certainly looked like one. Better still, we might get very close to it if we rowed carefully and quietly in that direction.

But as we drew nearer I thought the 'otter' looked peculiar. This animal's tail was bushy and floated high in the water.

My goodness – it was a squirrel! I had never seen a swimming squirrel before, and never expected to meet one in a mountain lake.

'Keep rowing, let's see if we can get really close,' I urged, and poor Alf did his best with the short oars in our awkward vessel. The squirrel stayed on the same course and did not appear to have noticed the presence of the rubber boat – or us.

We met in the middle of the lake and now the most surprising thing happened. Before we were quite aware of what was going on the squirrel had boarded us, via the rope which was fastened along the entire outside of the boat.

66

Squirrels are often 'left-handed', but that is no handicap.

Just a little trip to the top? — or a quick trip down to the ground?

Quickly it leaped along the edge, behind Alf's back, around the curve on to the 'far side of the field', and finally into the water, where it resumed its swim toward the other shore.

One should never underestimate a squirrel!

Maybe better to take the shortcut to the next tree!

THE SQUIRREL *(Sciurus vulgaris)* is found in all the woods of Norway. Sometimes it may be encountered in the high mountains, well above the tree level.
The squirrel's back is reddish brown in summer, grey, greyish blue or greyish brown in winter. The belly is always white. Its body is nine to ten inches long, the tail seven to eight inches (without hair).

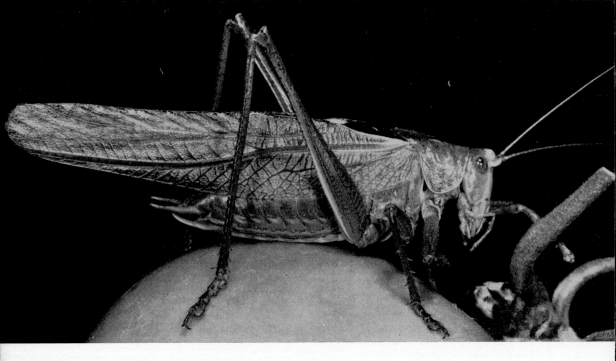

Musicians among the Leaves

Most people connect grasshoppers, locusts and other crickets with something strange and almost fantastic. This is to be expected. After all we were told stories while we were very young of the terrible swarms of locusts which laid the land waste and drove people away. Even in our times there are tales of grasshoppers ravaging. Scientists have only begun to find out how these enormous swarms develop.

We who live in parts of the world that are less exposed to the greed of grasshoppers, can hardly imagine what an enormous number there must be in a swarm, a number that of course can't be calculated. But to give you some idea I might mention that I read in a scientific treatise on insects that after a swarm of locusts had paid a

Adult long-horned grasshopper (male).

Grasshopper nymph (male) on a blue-bell. Behind its neck shield the small wing extensions protrude. Only after three to five skin changes will this be an adult cricket.

visit to Cyprus, something like 1,300 tons of locust eggs were collected. And I have tried for years here in Norway to find one single grasshopper egg!

So it is not so strange that these insects have a special place in human fantasy. Walt Disney with his exuberant cartoon has done much to illustrate the peculiarities of grasshoppers. I recall his film version of one of Æsop's most famous fables, 'The Ant and the Cricket'.

The bush cricket, or long-horned grass-hopper, measures two and a half inches from the forehead to the rear edge of its wings. This is an adult male. The 'musical instrument' is the dark spot just behind the neck shield, a sure sign that this is a male, shown also by the tongues at the tip of the back part of the body.

The bush cricket wings are folded aside, enabling us to see the musical instrument in detail. On the left wing cover there is a marked triangular area with distinct veins. One of these has a lot of fine hooks underneath. The round field of the right wing cover is the sounding board. Just by this there is a sharp edge, against which the left wing is rubbed.

'And what have you been doing this summer?' asked the ant, when the cricket came to borrow some food.

'Oh, I've fiddled and sung both day and night,' answered the cricket.

I don't know about the grasshopper's singing voice, but there is no doubt that it plays the 'violin'. Let's investigate its musical possibilities.

Among the leaves of bushes and trees we find the very audible long-horned grasshopper. It can be heard particularly on warm evenings in late summer. The sound may be so loud that one thinks it is made by a bird, but not everybody can hear it, as the frequency

73

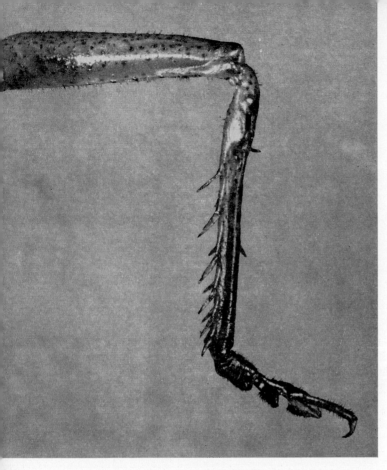

While short-horned grasshoppers' hearing organs are found on the first section of the rear body, the bush crickets' ears are located on the shins of the front legs. Here the ear is seen as a dark crack below the knee. Sounds are received when the front legs are placed in different positions.

is near the upper limit of what is audible to the human ear. Even though the sound seems to come from near by, the grasshopper may be sitting quite a distance away.

I have chosen the long-horned grasshopper (or bush cricket) as my subject, not only because its green hue may make it rather difficult to see and therefore more or less unknown to most people, but rather because of the musical instrument it uses, which is entirely different from that of the short-horned grasshopper, which many may have seen or at least heard or read about.

The short-horned grasshoppers stroke the thighs of their hind legs against the edge of the front wings, making a penetrating creaking sound, but the bush cricket plays entirely by means of its wings, without using its legs at all. To find out how this is possible one has to fold aside the front wings, which always lie one on top of the other, the left one uppermost. In the left wing there is a distinct triangular part with marked, strong veins. In a similar place in the right wing there is a round, thin membrane.

A very strong vein in the left wing is densely covered with fine hooks on the lower side. When the cricket moves this vein quickly back and forth against an edge of the right cover wing, both wings

Bush cricket (female) catching a moth. These crickets eat mostly other insects and are real preying beasts. They have no poison by which to kill their victims, only their strong jaws.

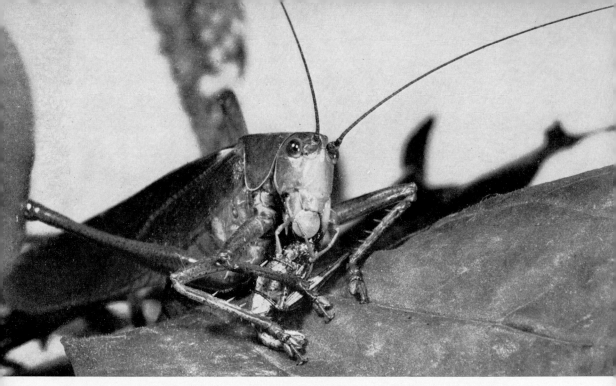

Big bush crickets don't mind attacking and eating their relatives. Here the victim is a short-horned grasshopper.

vibrate strongly, producing loud, quivering tones. The thin, round membrane in the right wing serves as a sounding-board and amplifies the tones, and the alluring music is made even louder when the cricket lifts its wings a little to form a sort of sound funnel.

Only the male cricket can make music. The female can listen, however, as they both have ears, only these ears are not mounted on their heads – but on the shins of their front legs! Thin ear-drums receive the sound waves from the vibrations of the wings. This hearing organ transmits the vibrations into nerve impulses which reach the brain via nerve fibres. By placing its front legs in various positions the cricket can tell where the music is coming from.

Why do we hear crickets playing only in late summer and in the autumn? This question must have been asked many times. Some

Close-up of a bush cricket. The powerful upper jaws look quite a bit like lobster claws. The big skin flap between them is the upper lip. At the top of the picture can be seen the big eyes, made up of thousands of facets.

This strange object is only part of a bush cricket. While showing a big cricket in a classroom one of my students was holding it on his hand, but when it suddenly bit him, he grabbed the insect with his free hand and threw it away. To our great surprise the head and some of its intestines remained on his hand. The head had fastened itself securely and remained alive for more than half an hour.

may believe that the crickets are born so late in the year that they are not able to perform earlier in the season, but this is not the case. Crickets are born in the early spring, but cannot produce any sounds until they are fully grown, some two or three months later. They need this time for their wings to develop. A young bush cricket has only small extensions behind the neck shield where the wings are fastened. To become adult the cricket has to go through 3-5 changes of skin – then the wings and their musical instrument are ready for use.

While short-horned grasshoppers are strict vegetarians, bush crickets on the whole feed mainly on other insects and are really beasts of prey. They have no poisonous secretions with which to kill their victims, but on the other hand their strong jaws can bite very hard.

It is said that bush crickets found in our latitudes are not able to bite through human skin, but this is not really true. I have proof that a cricket can do it. One of my students, a boy who was

This bigger type of bush cricket has got the popular Norwegian name 'wart-biter' because it was formerly believed that its strong jaws could bite away warts from human skin.

used to handling all sorts of strange animals, was helping me when I was about to show a big, very much alive leaf cricket to a special class at school. For some reason the cricket was irritated or scared, and the boy received a bite on the hand that made his whole body start. In a reflex motion he snatched the little animal off with his free hand. To his consternation the head didn't come away with the body, but remained on his hand and stayed alive without its body for more than half an hour.

So let's agree that crickets, locusts and other grasshoppers are very special animals.

BUSH CRICKETS *(Tettigoniidae)* belong to an insect family comprising more than 4,000 species, distributed over the greater part of the earth.

Bush cricket against a colourful background.

Deceptive Appearance

After a TV programme in which native snakes played the leading parts I received a number of odd calls and letters from viewers. Several of them felt that it was beneath my dignity as a school professor and a scientist to perform with live snakes. Stunts like that should be left to circus performers.

I am not going to venture into a discussion of people's reactions to snakes. This is a field where superstition and ignorance affect the viewpoint of the man in the street. Rather let me quote what a well-known Danish zoologist writes in the foreword of a very comprehensive book on reptiles:

The birth of grass snakes! One egg can already be seen on the ground, the next is on its way out.

The grass snake is an excellent swimmer and can stay under the surface for more than half an hour. It lives mostly among the reeds on a lake shore and feeds on frogs and small fish.

'Even in the modest and not very attractive surroundings of the terrarium (the 'Snake House' of the Zoo in Copenhagen) its inhabitants, the big crocodiles, the enormous boa constrictors and the dangerous venomous snakes never fail to exert a certain attraction, a strange mixture of revolt and awe. A feeling of something exotic seizes one at the sight and smell of these animals which we have no opportunities in Denmark of studying in their natural habitat.' He writes further about the study of reptiles: '– This study attains a peculiar perspective when one considers that the reptiles were the first vertebrates which freed themselves entirely from the water, that they were once the ruling class of animals on earth, from which both birds and mammals originated.'

Let us agree that snakes play an important part in the animal life of this world. In Norway there can be found only three types of the almost three thousand different snakes which exist. Can't we then afford to treat them with a little tolerance and understanding?

In this chapter I'm going to talk about two snakes that are quite harmless, but as they are often mistaken for vipers they die unnecessarily. In this connection I might mention an episode which took place last spring.

The route to his office took a neighbour of mine close to a place where for quite some time there have been a great number of smooth snakes. One morning he noticed a magpie diving down to attack something which turned out to be a smooth snake, and which it proceeded to kill and eat in short order. We humans make mistakes,

Such is life! A grass snake has caught a frog and proceeds to eat it alive. It can't kill its victim first, but there is nothing wrong with its appetite, and it will gladly eat three or four frogs in one meal.

but a magpie seems to know the difference between a smooth snake and a viper. It would never have dared to attack the latter.

When people tell me that they have seen giant vipers, much bigger than ever reported before from the districts in question, one can safely assume that they have seen *grass snakes*.

The most prominent characteristic of the grass snake is two yellow spots on its neck. They are usually so marked that they are visible from afar. Admittedly some grass snakes are all black or greyish black, and some all-black vipers have been found – specimens without a visible zig-zag band along the back – so mistakes are bound to be made.

To avoid making them – look the snake in the eye! If the pupils are like slits, they belong to a viper – if they are round, you are looking at a grass snake or smooth snake.

The eyes of snakes are altogether rather peculiar. The lower eyelid is always pulled up to cover the cornea and joined to the upper lid

Of all reptiles found in Norway the grass snake is the only one which lays eggs. It is very productive – ten to fifteen eggs are the rule and double that is no rarity. Often several females lay their eggs in the same spot.

A smooth snake showing off its tongue. It is thought that snakes display their tongues this way to absorb taste and smell from their surroundings. The tongue has no sensory cells for taste and smell, but when it is pulled in the two points are brought into two small canals in the roof of the oral cavity, where any smell or taste impressions are brought into contact with corresponding cells. When the snake stretches out its tongue the mouth is closed, but the jaws don't quite meet in front, making room for the tongue to protrude.

by a transparent membrane which resembles the cornea. For this reason snakes cannot blink their eyes – which in a way always remain shut – and this accounts for their staring gaze. Previously it was believed that this gaze had hypnotic power to paralyze the poor victims. Today scientists think that the snake causes a simple 'terror reaction' by fixating its victims.

The grass snake lives mostly in swampy surroundings, particularly near lakes where there are plenty of reeds along the shores. Its favourite food consists of frogs and small fish, and it is an excellent swimmer, staying under water for more than half an hour at a time.

The grass snake is the biggest snake in our part of the world. Not infrequently it attains a length of more than three feet, but in Southern Europe specimens of more than 7 feet have been found.

Although the grass snake has no venomous teeth, it still has a rather efficient means of keeping an attacker at bay. It can project a yellow, vile-smelling liquid through its anal opening. Anyone getting this on his clothes may as well send them to the cleaners at once.

This, by the way was the cause of a very surprising and amusing incident once when a friend and I were dealing with a grass snake. He stretched out his arm to grab the snake by its tail, but before his hand had reached it, the grass snake lifted its tail, fired – – and hit its mark!

The smooth snake, too, is often mistaken for a viper, as these snakes are roughly the same size. Two rows of small, black-brown spots along the back of the smooth snake often blend together to form a ribbon similar to the zig-zag ribbon of the viper, making it even harder to tell one from the other.

How then can one distinguish between viper and smooth snake? One sure, unmistakable characteristic of the smooth snake is a distinct dark band from its nostril to its neck. And furthermore the shells on its body are quite smooth, without any longitudinal ridge like those of the viper or the grass snake.

The smooth snake has very strong muscles and is an excellent climber. In this respect it is not far behind its tropical relatives. In the daytime it usually keeps quiet, but at night it goes hunting. It feeds mostly on shrew mice and other small rodents, or small birds, but will also eat frogs, blind-worms and lizards. When killing its victim it acts like a real boa constrictor.

The body strength of a smooth snake is impressive, but it is its only means of defense. I remember when I first picked up a smooth snake with my bare hands, how its violent contortions made me drop it. It is really quite temperamental and doesn't hesitate to bite, but its bite is quite harmless and the snake soon becomes quiet and

The smooth snake is an excellent climber, nearly an equal of its more famous tropical relatives. This harmless snake has great bodily strength and acts like a boa constrictor when overpowering its victim.

This serious-looking young man is not worried about what is going on, except that he is concerned that his beloved smooth snake will get away from him and disappear. Smooth snakes soon become docile and manageable and are quite harmless to humans.

The name of the smooth snake is derived from the fact that its body shells are smooth, without any longitudinal ridges.

docile. Most smooth snakes which I have had at home have enjoyed twining themselves around my neck and arms. Some have even made their way inside my shirt at the neck, twisting downward underneath my clothes to emerge through one trouser leg!

THE GRASS SNAKE *(Natrix natrix)* is the biggest snake in Norway where it often attains a length of three to four feet. In Southern Europe it may become more than seven feet long.

On the upper side it is usually olive grey, but can be greyish or bluish black. The lower part of its head and neck is light yellowish white, while the belly is light with dark spots. Special characteristic: two pale yellow spots, one on each side of the head.

THE SMOOTH SNAKE *(Coronella austriaca)* is rarely more than thirty inches long. This snake seems to be regressing pronouncedly in Norway, while it is quite common in Middle Europe.

The upper side of this snake is yellowish or greyish brown, while the belly is grey-blue. Special characteristic: a dark ribbon from the nostril through the eye to the neck.

Strange Sleeping Quarters

'Daddy, where do the little birds sleep at night?' Is there a father who hasn't at some time or other been asked this question? And is there on the other hand a father who could give the right answer without hesitation the first time he was asked?

I can well remember how my little daughter, Trine, had me stumped. She was standing on a stool by the kitchen window, looking at the bird tray outside with her nose pressed against the pane. The birds were flying to and fro. One picked sunflower seeds, another took some hemp seeds and then they dashed over to the frozen, icy branches of the lilac bush on the other side of the yard to enjoy their meal.

Well, where *did* these winter guests really sit down to sleep? I ought to know, but frankly I had never thought about it. And strangely enough I had never encountered sleeping birds, in spite of all my poking into corners and cracks. I had mainly been hunting for bats, but nevertheless – –.

I had to confess my ignorance and tell the child that I didn't know where the birds spent their nights. Trine suggested that they might use her doll's bed, and as I didn't like to give her an outright no for an answer, I told her I would make a real bird-house for the birds to sleep in.

It struck me suddenly that my faithful helper Karsten often had overnight guests in his bird-houses. This is why he lets them hang outside all winter, while most people take them in in the late autumn. I usually did the same thing myself, but perhaps now I'd better try Karsten's system – or preferably something even better.

A great tit fast asleep on a twig.

I went on to promise Trine that the birds would have a real bed-room with a big window, to let us peek in on them when they slept. She shouted with joy and I just hoped that I wouldn't have to disappoint her, as I wasn't quite sure what I had let myself in for.

We went down into the basement right away. On a shelf I found an observation box with transparent plastic forming one entire wall. Trine agreed that this would make a fine bird's house, but what about a mattress for them to sleep on? Oh yes, I would make them beds with fine, dry grass, but I didn't want her doll's bed. The birds might be scared by such a strange object. I secretly hoped that the birds would like something to sleep on – but for all I knew they might sleep standing on one leg.

When the plastic wall was fitted into place I covered it with a dark cloth to make the box as dark inside as an ordinary bird-box. Then we carried it out and put it up in a maple tree close by the lilac bush, at a suitable height for Trine and me to stand on a small ladder and look in through the plastic window.

As it grew darker outside Trine stood on her stool and gazed in tense expectation across the yard. The kitchen window got a lot of new marks from her nose and fingers.

But as it darkened the birds disappeared without any of them showing any interest whatsoever in the fine house we had made for them.

Trine was quite inconsolable. When I carried her up to her bed I had to promise to take her out to Karsten the next morning, to hang our bird bedroom there. In his peaceful little valley the birds are used to sleeping in bird-houses, and if only we were patient we would surely see some overnight guests in our house.

Next morning Trine's grandmother paid us an unexpected visit, and in her delight over this, my little daughter forgot both the birds and my solemn promise to take her to Karsten. It couldn't have suited me better.

A tit inspecting its home. In a minute it will dash inside. Bird-houses hanging outside in the winter often serve as sleeping quarters for titmice and other cave-dwellers among small birds. Bird lovers generally know this and therefore hang up their bird-houses again after autumn cleaning. Their inhabitants don't mind if they get a little dry grass or sawdust in the bottom of the box to keep the room warmer and absorb moist refuse.

As soon as I came home from school I sneaked the observation box into my car and got away undetected. It was still daylight when I parked my old jalopy in Karsten's courtyard.

It was bitterly cold, nearly 15° below zero, but didn't feel as severe here in the woods as in town, where the river and the fjord make the air humid and raw.

On Karsten's bird tray traffic was heavy today. He certainly looked after his friends. Tallow, butter, cheese and oats were served.

'Well, Per, does the food look good enough for you?'

It was Karsten who suddenly appeared behind me, carrying a big armful of firewood.

93

Safely inside, the great tit yawns a little and blows up its feathers.

It looks as if the head is tucked underneath the wing, but it really is stuck beneath breast and back feathers covering the wing.

Almost a perfect feather ball. The legs are not visible at all, but the tit doesn't stand on one leg like a chicken when it sleeps.

Even the tit has to change position while sleeping. Here the head is tucked in beneath the feathers on the other side.

'Good enough – why, you feed the birds as if they don't have any of their own fat reserves left,' I replied.

This was just what Karsten had counted on. The last part of the winter, from the end of January, is the most critical time for small birds in our northern latitudes. Then their fat reserves underneath the skin dwindle rapidly.

Karsten showed me in and I settled myself in a comfortable chair by the window with a direct view of the bird tray. While my host lit a fire and made coffee I told him the main purpose of my visit. He smiled when he saw my observation box. Oh no, that one wouldn't do for *his* birds to sleep in. They were used to 'real houses'.

But as we started to discuss bird-houses he had to tell me of a change in the birds' habits. As I had seen, he had several boxes outside, but as far as he could tell, only one of them was used by the birds as sleeping quarters – the one hanging in a birch tree by the out-house. He had seen a titmouse dash in every now and then. But all the other boxes were empty and unused.

The small birds had started instead to seek refuge under the roof tiles. They are of the old-fashioned curved kind which offer many excellent openings where small birds can easily get in.

Could I explain to him why this was so?

My conclusion was that the birds just by chance had decided that they preferred the new abode. The birds who still used the bird-house by the birch tree probably didn't know any better, being more or less chance guests on the premises.

Karsten didn't agree. There must be some other explanation. He could tell me that the flock of birds was diminishing much faster than before. In earlier years the small birds had been more numerous and lively at this time. Furthermore he knew that a sparrow hawk was a steady 'customer' here. It came regularly to pick up a bird just after dawn and another just after dusk in the afternoon.

The pigmy owl often uses a bird-house as sleeping quarters.

Karsten had noticed this on Sundays, when he didn't have to get up before dawn to go to work. The hawk came down like lightning among the birds on the tray, scattering them in all directions and picking its victim, usually one which headed for the thorny bushes across the meadows, but was caught in the hawk's talons before it could make it.

But one sparrow hawk alone could hardly reduce the number of small birds that drastically. There are quite a few non-migrating birds in this valley. Karsten was sure that as soon as one bird was caught by the hawk another came to take its place, one that had wanted to get the easy pickings but hadn't had a chance before.

In other words there must be several birds of prey decimating Karsten's little guests – the whole neighbourhood would soon be empty of small birds. But what kind of birds of prey? Karsten had no idea.

Suddenly I was sure I had the answer. There could be no other explanation.

'Tell me, Karsten,' I asked him, 'can you get that bird-house down from the tree now? It isn't too dark outside yet?'

Karsten looked at me uncomprehendingly.

'What do you want to do with that – *now?*'

'Just wait, I may be able to explain the whole mystery.'

Karsten is quick and nimble and before long he was back in the living room with the bird-house – a big box with a roomy entrance. The roof could be twisted to one side and it was an easy matter for Karsten to turn the box upside down and empty its contents on to a newspaper on the floor.

And what contents! Here were left-overs from many meals.

'I do declare I must have had a pigmy owl as a visitor here this winter,' Karsten said as he fished a regurgitated pellet out from the mass of feathers.

97

Titmice have to be on the lookout for food constantly during the winter when supplies are scarce. Here a dead waxwing is being consumed.

The pigmy owl is not much bigger than a bullfinch, but can cause havoc among small birds. Here a sparrow is the victim.

The pigmy owl, smallest among the owls of Europe, has often been called a brigand in miniature. It weighs no more than two or two and a half ounces, yet it exacts its tribute at dusk or dawn, or even in the middle of the day. In winter it kills more birds than it can eat in one meal, yet very little is wasted as the pigmy owl hoards all remnants.

'Maybe not just one,' I answered as I sorted feathers out from various titmice – the sad remnants of those birds who had been the most frequent guests on the tray outside the window.

'Can you imagine why I didn't think of this myself?' said Karsten. 'I know so well that the pigmy owl hoards small birds as winter supplies. Very up-to-date, too – keeping them in a deep-freeze!'

The heap of feathers was quite firmly compressed. Apparently the owl had made itself comfortable in the box. I thought of Trine and her touching suggestion of putting her doll's bed into the box for the

This can be the fate of small birds staying in or near a bird-house in winter. Most of this heap of feathers was quite hard, and the pigmy owl had more than a dozen birds in its 'deep freeze'.

small birds to sleep in. It was a good thing that she had stayed home. It isn't always so easy to explain to small children why life sometimes seems so brutal.

However, Trine was going to see a small bird asleep, though I can hardly take the credit for it.

About a week after my visit to Karsten there was a knock on the kitchen door one evening. One of my young students came in. He carried a shoe-box, and inside there was a great tit, blowing out its feathers until it appeared as round as a ball.

The boy had found the tit in the snow by the roadside, and he

The sparrow hawk has phenomenal eye-sight, and any intended victim has very little chance of escaping.

A great tit was too slow and ended in the clutches of the sparrow hawk's terrible talons.

was sure it must be sick, because it didn't seem to be able to fly. Couldn't I look after it and make it well again?

I praised him for his consideration and promised to do what I could, but I knew that it was doubtful that I could do much. When a bird has reached this condition it usually dies within a few hours. However, we could always hope. The boy thanked me and left.

In the basement I had a spare bird tray. I put the same kind of food there as I had seen on Karsten's tray, and placed a saucer full of water beside it. Trine knew nothing about all this. She was already getting ready for bed upstairs when the boy came with the tit. But next morning I took her down to show her the bird.

The sparrow hawk plucking its victim while holding it with its claws, tearing feathers out with its beak.

We looked everywhere for it – in vain, at first however. My house is quite old, part of it – including the basement – was built more than two hundred years ago, and there are plenty of holes and cracks where small animals can hide. So we continued our search.

There it was! Suddenly I caught sight of it. On a beam just underneath the ceiling it sat – fast asleep.

I lifted up Trine to let her see the little ball, sitting there with its head hidden in a pretty little bouquet of feathers. Here and now I could verify that birds do *not* sleep with their heads tucked underneath their wings.

I also noticed another fact I had not known before. The tit was

Here a mouse is caught in the hawk's talons.

resting on the whole length of the tarsus, in other words more or less lying on its belly. Now I know that this is the usual sleeping position for small birds resting on a floor or board.

I whispered to Trine to be quiet, but she was so excited that she shouted with joy and delight. The bird showed no reaction, however, and there was no doubt that it was very sick. I told Trine that we had to wait before we put it out into the box in the maple tree. We mustn't wake up the poor little sick bird.

That afternoon the tit was dead.

THE GREAT TIT *(Parus major)* is common as a brooder in Norway as far north as the Polar Circle. It is stationary, but the young birds often stray a little in winter, and some leave the country in October to return in the late winter months.

The breast and sides are yellow, the cheeks white and head and throat are black, while its back is bluish green and the wings bluegrey with white ribbons across. Along the breast there is a darker stripe.

The great tit lays its eggs in April–May, from six to fourteen at a time.

THE PIGMY OWL *(Glaucidium passerinum)* is mostly found in Eastern Norway, also as a brooder. It is stationary as well as migrating, and the nests are rarely found.

Its upper side is dark brown with white spots, the tail has some white cross-stripes, and underneath it is white with brown spots. The pigmy owl is a little bigger than a sparrow, six to eight inches long with wings of four to four and a half inches. Eggs are laid in April–May, three to eight at a time.

The pigmy owl eats mostly small birds and rodents. It is the only owl that hoards winter supplies of food.

THE SPARROW HAWK *(Accipiter nisus)* appears as a brooder in most parts of Norway. It migrates, but some individuals are stationary in winter.

Like the goshawk the male and female differ considerably in size. The male is about as big as a big thrush, while the female is the size of a pigeon. Eggs are laid in late April or in May, usually four or five at a time.

The sparrow hawk eats mostly small birds, but conditions permitting, small rodents are included in the meals.

A Brief Moment on White Wings

In Norway, if adults are asked what a cabbage caterpillar really is, I am afraid that many either give the wrong answer or just don't know. School children are usually better informed. For the record, let us say here that it is the larva that is changed into a beautiful, white-winged insect known by everyone – the cabbage butterfly.

Unfortunately it is very common in Norway to call larvae 'worms'. I would rather we stick to the good old term *larva*, a Latin word meaning ghost or mask. It is easy to see why this word was used in connection with insects. At the larva stage many insects are so 'masked' that these 'ghosts' bear no resemblance at all to the finished insects into which they are to become transformed some day. In butterflies this transformation is complete, and the cabbage butterfly is a familiar and good illustration of this.

As we are talking about the transformation process it seems natural to use another term of Latin origin – *pupa*, meaning more or less a swathed infant. All insects undergoing a complete transformation, go through a pupal stage in their development. This is a resting period, when the larva is changed into a finished insect, or *imago*. At the pupal stage a revolution takes place in the insect body. This is evident from pictures of the larva before it spins its cocoon – compared with pictures of the wonderful newly-hatched insect taking to its wings.

Although it has nothing to do with the cabbage butterfly, I am tempted to bring in still another term of foreign origin, the Greek word *nymph*. It was first used as a name for half immortal young maidens who lived in the woods. Among insects the word is used for

The big cabbage butterfly has snow-white wings with a triangular black spot on each front wing-tip. The female is usually larger than the male. The cabbage butterfly is one of our largest day butterflies, and the wing span can be up to 2 ½ inches.

the young of those that undergo what is called an incomplete transformation. These youngsters are very similar to adults. A typical example is a young grasshopper which looks like nothing else but an adult grasshopper. Insects undergoing an incomplete transformation are to a greater or lesser extent cast in the same mould from the time they leave the egg, and the development to a finished insect takes place through successive changes of skin.

Most butterfly larvae feed on green leaves. The caterpillar is not unique in this respect, but it can be a great nuisance to farmers and horticulturists through its ravaging in the fields and among plants. However, quite likely the caterpillar is sometimes blamed for misdeeds of which it isn't guilty. Cabbage plants disfigured by large and small irregular holes in their leaves and criss-crossed by slimy trails have not been attacked by caterpillars, but by snails. Field snails have eating orgies too.

Men have always been engaged in a constant struggle against insects attacking cultured plants. With all due respect to the effects of DDT and other insecticides it must be admitted that so far insects have held their own pretty well in this struggle. But there are also examples of men using insects to protect themselves against other threatening pests. In the nineteenth century a strange cactus plant was introduced into Australia. In its new surroundings this plant spread incredibly fast. Finally it had changed about sixty million acres of the best and most fertile land into an impenetrable bush.

A great number of cactus-eating insects were mobilized in the fight, but to no avail. About forty years ago, however, an Argentine butterfly larva was found to be effective against this cactus, and today most of the lost land has been reclaimed. Many Australians understandably think that this butterfly is the most useful animal in the world.

Cabbage butterfly laying its eggs. The female presses her sensitive hind body against the cabbage leaf and the eggs are squeezed out one by one.

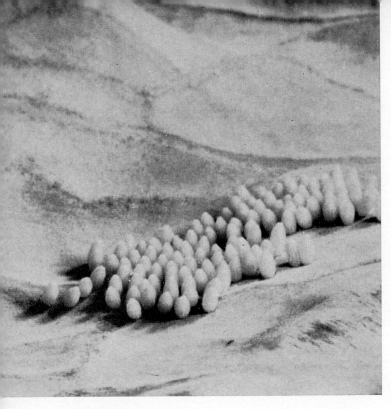

The female butterfly flies from plant to plant while laying her eggs. 25-50 eggs are laid in each place. When the laying is finished, her purpose is fulfilled. On this plant she has really been busy and has left some 100 eggs. Altogether she lays 200-300.

But let us return to our part of the world and its cabbage butterflies. There are just two generations a year, as the climate will allow no more. The generation which is born in late summer, has to hibernate in the pupal stage. Under normal conditions it isn't hatched until late next spring, so other butterflies have to herald the coming of spring.

Once I thought for a while that these facts were getting a bit topsy-turvy. One of my school colleagues brought me a butterfly one day in the middle of March. His son had found it and put it in a box, and now insisted that I see it.

Frankly I wasn't too excited about the contents of the box. The butterfly was probably one of the 'sensational finds' that swamp newspaper editors and zoologists just at this time. But when my colleague said that the butterfly was white, I lost no time in getting the lid off.

It was really rather a sensation, as the box contained a specimen of the large cabbage butterfly. It must have been born at least six weeks too early. How could this be?

I asked my friend what sort of vegetables he kept in his garden. No cabbage, he said, and no cabbage fields closer than a quarter of a mile away.

Still – that field must be the explanation. There this butterfly must have been born some time in July or August the year before. As a larva it had eaten and grown big there, and then it had made its way across grass and gravel, finally getting into the house through the kitchen door or an open window. Finding a safe place to enter the pupal stage it had gone to rest for the winter.

But at this stage it is not prepared for the artificial heat in our houses in winter. Its life rhythm was disturbed and so as a butterfly

It takes from a week to a fortnight for the egg-shells to break and the larvae to come out. New-born caterpillars are less than a twelfth of an inch long. They have black heads and pale yellow bodies, covered with fairly long white hair. Their jaws are very powerful, enabling them to crack the egg shells.

it left its pupal cocoon many weeks before the time this was meant to happen. Now it was in my care. I helped it turn back the calendar by cooling it off carefully and putting it to sleep once more. One sunny day in May I could open my window and send it out to fly on white wings across green meadows.

The hectic life of a cabbage butterfly lasts but three to four weeks. During this brief period its two main purposes are to find food – and to find a mate. Food is plentiful, as most spring flowers contain nectar (floral honey), the only form of food butterflies eat.

Finding a mate is sometimes not so simple, as relatively few individuals survive the winter. The courtship is further encumbered by the fact that the male can't find a mate among the right type of white butterflies by sight alone until he is at close quarters. Like all other day butterflies, the cabbage butterfly is very shortsighted. To guide their suitors the females spread a special scent from glands in

Here the caterpillars have changed their first skin. Visible growth takes place only for a short time after the change, while the new skin is stretched.

Caterpillars after the second skin change. The discarded skins are clearly visible. These larvae are six to eight days old.

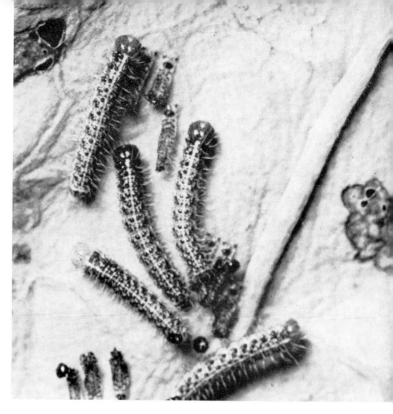

their hind bodies, a scent which is registered by the antennae of the males. The males can, on the other hand, attract the females by producing a special scent in shells on the upper side of their front wings.

When contact has been established and mating accomplished the female flies away to find a suitable place to lay her eggs. She usually selects the under-side of a leaf. At first she touches the surface of the leaf with the point of her hind body, then she lifts this part a little, and an egg is pressed out. It is immediately pressed against the leaf and sticks there. The next egg may be laid on another plant, but often the butterfly lays several eggs in the same spot, where they form a small heap.

The cabbage butterfly lays 200–300 eggs in all before dying. The eggs are shaped like short, thick bullets pointing upwards. In 8–14

113

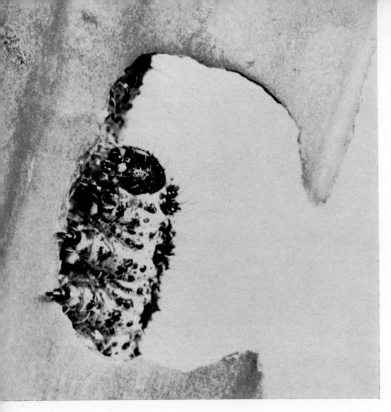

Caterpillar gorging itself on a cabbage plant. When these greedy creatures eat simultaneously one can actually hear their chewing several yards away.

days, depending on conditions, the eggs are hatched and the larvae appear. They eat their way out of their shells, and the process takes ten minutes or more.

For a couple of days the larvae stay close together near the egg-shells. They may lie quietly for a long while, then, as if at a signal, they start gnawing their shells, and eventually, still simultaneously, they stop and rest again.

After two to three days they no longer eat shells, but change to a vegetarian diet consisting of leaves. In another three to four days they change their skins for the first time. In this second stage the typical pattern becomes evident: a yellow line along the back, black spots on the sides, against a pale green base colour. The larvae don't stay as close together, and start to eat through the leaves.

Two days after the first skin change the larvae are about three

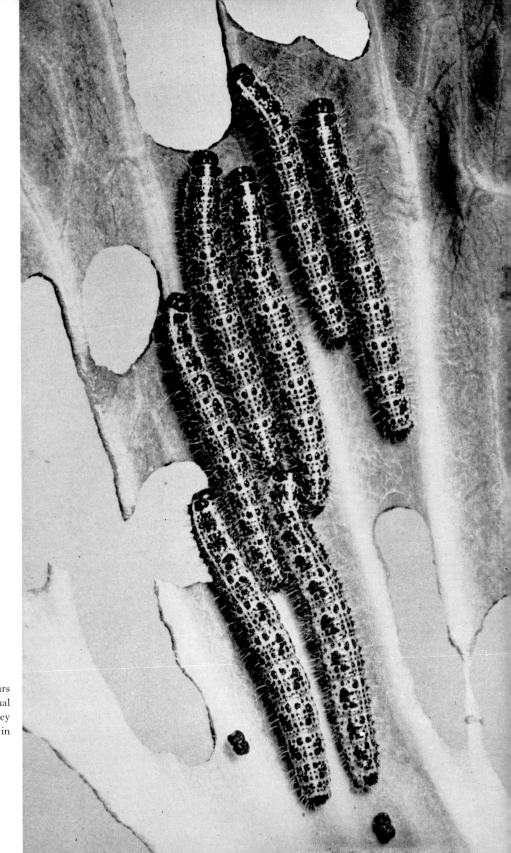

Adult caterpillars (twice their actual size). Normally they grow to be adult in three weeks.

When the larvae are about to enter the pupal stage, they wander around to find suitable places for the impending process. Larvae of the spring generation, that are to be hatched in late summer, settle as pupae among plants, but those born so late that they hibernate, have to seek more protected places like overhanging roofs, attics, fence-posts or crevices. The pictures show their behaviour when preparing for and entering the pupal stage:

eighths of an inch long while they were less than one eighth of an inch when they were born. Visible growth occurs only just after the skin change, while the new skin is stretched. This skin is formed underneath the old, and is roomier, therefore it lies in loose folds.

The length of the growing period depends on weather conditions. Normally the caterpillar reaches its adult stage in three weeks. It is then about one and a half inches long and nearly a quarter of an inch

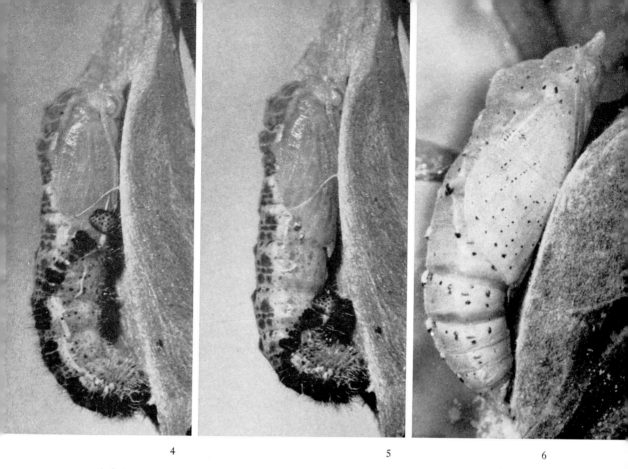

1. Spinning a silk cushion on the leaf under the point of its hind body and a 'safety belt' around itself. 2. A day later raising its 'neck', making the skin crack and the pupa appear. 3. The pupa works its body out. Embryo eyes, antennae and wings become visible. 4. The larva skin turned down *underneath* the 'safety belt'. 5. Skin almost completely removed. 6. The trick completed. Disrobed pupa hangs ready for sleep.

thick. For a few days after their last skin change the larvae eat colossally, but the appetite diminishes as the pupal stage approaches. Just before this time the larvae seem to roam restlessly on their leaves, obviously seeking suitable places for their rest. The generation which was born in the spring enters the pupal stage usually among the plants. The pupal stage then lasts only a couple of weeks, whereupon the butterfly appears.

Butterflies hatched in summer are naturally far more numerous than those hatched from hibernating pupae the following spring. In very dry summers the second generation may become so numerous that often one sees large swarms of white-winged beauties flying over cabbage fields and meadows and gardens in bloom. The females of this generation prefer to lay their eggs on leaves of cultured plants like beets or cabbage, and if the larvae get favourable living conditions, extensive damage can be caused to the crops.

Often the larvae eat so prodigiously that only the main veins of the leaves remain on many plants.

Caterpillars born of the second generation don't seek plants for their pupal stage. They are going to hibernate, and so they go for places offering better protection, such as overhanging roofs, wooden fences, brick or wooden walls, rock crevices or attics in houses.

But even if conditions are very favourable, relatively few of these caterpillars will reach the hibernating stage. Most of them become victims of thrushes or starlings, sparrows or crows – not to mention a small parasite wasp which likes to lay its eggs in the body of the caterpillar, causing it to die from intestinal worms!

THE BIG CABBAGE BUTTERFLY *(Pieris brassicae)* is common all over Norway. The biggest individuals have wing spans of two and a half inches. The wings are snow-white with black triangular spots at the front wing-tips. The female also has some black spots in the middle of the wings.

The larvae normally grow to their full size in three weeks. They are then one and a half inches long and three sixteenths of an inch thick. Larvae of the spring generation are hatched to become flying insects after a pupal stage lasting about two weeks, while the pupae of the late summer generation hibernate.

Slow ashore – quick submerged

Salamanders? Aren't they those long-tailed creatures darting about in the sun, in the grass or along a wall? Some kind of lizard? I have received answers like these very often, and they aren't all that crazy, even though they are far from correct. In appearance salamanders, or newts, are quite a bit like lizards, and furthermore they are called water lizards in many places.

But there is more of a difference than meets the eye. To begin

Digging for hibernating newts.

119

with, salamanders are not reptiles like lizards. They are amphibious animals, an entirely different group. Amphibious (from the Greek words *amphi:* in two ways, and *bios:* life) animals are made to live partly in water, partly on dry land. Lizards are pure land animals that love sunlight and warmth, while salamanders are mainly water animals, staying mostly by ponds, puddles and small water-holes. In water they move freely and nimbly, while they are slow and awkward on land.

Salamanders have a soft and slimy skin like all other amphibians, and their toes have no claws, while lizards have shells all over their skin and sharp claws on their toes.

Salamanders are rarely seen on land. In the day-time they usually hide under rocks or tree-roots in dark, shady places. Toward night-fall they venture forth to hunt for food, mostly insects, worms and snails.

Newts are members of the salamander family commonly found in this country. I well remember the first time I was looking for them

The common newt crawling out of its hibernating place. It is quite puzzling how newts with their fragile limbs manage to dig down to depths where they don't freeze in winter. This one hibernated in clay.

Big female crested newt seen from beneath.

Crested newt couple in wedding attire. The male is easily recognisable by its dorsal crest, which is very high and crenated in the mating season.

on their way from their hibernating place to the breeding pond. For three days in a row I stayed near a small lake in a wood. Not until the third evening, when I had more or less given up hope and was preparing to go home, did I see one of the big crested newts on the shore. With slow movements it crawled toward the water's edge.

Delighted as a child I picked it up and put it on my hand, stroking its back several times. I let it crawl along my arm all the way to my shoulder. Its skin was dry, its belly empty and the whole body emaciated. A fold of the skin on the back hung loosely along one side, proving that I surely had got hold of a male newt, as this fold was the beginning of a dorsal comb or crest.

I walked over to the water and slipped the animal in. What a transformation! With graceful undulations of the body and tail it shot forward through the water. All four legs were held close to the body and the dorsal crest pointed straight upwards.

And there was more to be seen in the water. Near the shore a big female was 'parked'. One front leg rested lightly on some algae and the animal appeared to be sleeping. But a slight movement of one eye showed it was not. A mosquito larva came bouncing up through the water nearby, a victim the newt was waiting for. Slowly it moved its head into the right position, and ... in a flash the larva had disappeared into its mouth. A couple of swimming strokes with the tail and the newt was in position by another plant. There seemed to be plenty of food in the lake, even this early in the spring.

Later that year I frequently visited the lake and saw several newts. One day a male was swimming along with a thin piece of skin hanging from one hind leg. I fished the animal up in my net, pulled off the piece and let the newt go. When I threw the piece of skin into the

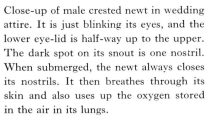

Close-up of male crested newt in wedding attire. It is just blinking its eyes, and the lower eye-lid is half-way up to the upper. The dark spot on its snout is one nostril. When submerged, the newt always closes its nostrils. It then breathes through its skin and also uses up the oxygen stored in the air in its lungs.

lake it filled completely with water and took on the form of a complete skin, with body, legs, tail and head.

Newts change their skin several times during the spring, and their appearance is changed each time. The colours become fresher, the males' dorsal crests increase and their tails widen. The female, too, develops an edge to its tail, but not so big.

When mating time approaches, the newts have been in the water for about a month. Each male then selects one female which he pursues and tries to impress for hours, even days. When the courtship is over and spawning starts, the male presses a jellified capsule of sperm – a spermatophore – out through its anal opening, and fastens the capsule to a rock or some other firm base. Then the female crawls over this sperm mass and by means of muscular contractions she presses the sperm into her own anal opening, to fertilize the eggs.

The eggs are laid one at a time and usually fastened to a water plant leaf. I observed a female laying eggs in summer. With one hind

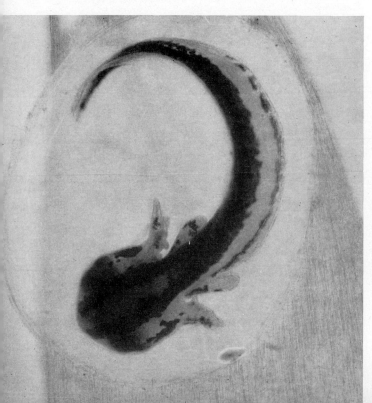

Eight days old foetus of crested newt in its egg capsule which is fastened to a leaf under water. The capsule is filled with a liquid and is firm. The embryo is seen from behind. Beginnings of outer gills are found on both sides of the spherical head.

Fully grown larva of crested newt. Through capillary veins in the big outer gills the larvae breathe like fish, and simultaneously breathe through their thin skin.

leg she pressed a leaf against her anal opening, and soon an oblong, pale yellow egg was pressed out, a thin jelly-membrane sticking it to the leaf.

I took one of these eggs home with me and put it in my aquarium. After two weeks the foetus was fully developed within the egg capsule. It was about a quarter of an inch long. On the fifteenth day it started to twist and turn violently, beating its tail back and forth. Suddenly the capsule broke and the animal made its way clear of it and let itself sink to the bottom of the aquarium.

In another week the gills, the beginnings of which had been visible for some time, had grown to large, feathery organs on each side of the head, and the front and hind legs had grown out, the front

This incredible countenance belongs to the newt larva seen in profile on the preceding page. Notice the wide mouth. These larvae are very greedy and often attack each other if food is scarce. But it doesn't matter much if a tail or leg is lost, as these are regenerated in a very short time.

limbs first. The larva looked quite fantastic, especially from the front.

In a couple of months the larva had grown to its full size in the aquarium, and I moved it to its home in the lake in the woods. Perhaps it still lives there?

THE CRESTED NEWT *(Triturus cristatus)* can be as much as six inches long and some have been reported to become very old. One individual in captivity is said to have reached the age of 22 years.

THE COMMON NEWT *(Triturus vulgaris)* rarely exceeds three inches in length, and its skin is smooth.

Contents